Unleash Your Pitching
VELOCITY

THE 3-STEP SYSTEM TO THROWING HARDER AND MAXIMIZING COMMAND SO YOU CAN MAKE THE TEAM OF YOUR DREAMS

DR. CHRIS MCKENZIE

www.UnleashPitchingVelocity.com

Disclaimer: The information provided in this book is designed to provide helpful information on the subjects discussed. This book is not meant to be used, nor should it be used, to diagnose or treat any medical condition. For diagnosis or treatment of any medical problem, consult your own primary healthcare provider. The publisher and author are not responsible for any specific health or allergy needs that may require medical supervision and are not liable for any damages or negative consequences from any treatment, action, application or preparation, to any person reading or following the information in this book. This book is sold with the understanding that the author and publisher are not rendering medical, health, or personal services. References are provided for informational purposes only and do not constitute endorsement of any websites or other sources. Readers should be aware that the websites listed in this book may change.

Cover Design by: Tanja Prokop www.bookcoverworld.com

Illustrations by: @Inkstown on Instagram

Interior Photography by: Chris Sheehan www.chrissheehan.com

Back Cover Photography by: Jeff Berkes www.jeffberkes.com

ISBN: 978-1-7322624-4-7

DEDICATION

This book is dedicated to my wife, Emma, and my parents, Michele and Greg. I cannot thank you enough for your love, your continued belief in me, and your never-ending support of all the craziness I undertake in my life, including the long and oftentimes all-consuming book writing process.

To my son, Graham, in life you have to take risks to get where you want to go. Make sure they are calculated, but take them. Learn from your mistakes and prosper from the wins. May you have the courage to take risks to share your gifts with the world.

God bless you. I love you.

PRAISE FOR "UNLEASH YOUR PITCHING VELOCITY"

"I'm a big fan of Dr. McKenzie's work, and he doesn't disappoint with this title. I've had a chance to review the book and the first thing that came to mind was 'Pitching Science for Dummies' because of his unique way of making the complex, simple. If you're serious about developing as a pitcher, learning more as a coach, or educating yourself as a parent on what it truly takes for the body to throw a baseball, this is the book for you."

—Lantz Wheeler, www.baseballthinktank.com

"Because of his understanding as an athlete who's had to deal with injury and setback, this has given Chris tremendous insight and ability to help baseball players. He's lived it. He went through it. This book lays out a simple process that will allow ANY pitcher to optimize their performance, minimize injury, and stay healthy for the long term."

—Alan Jaeger, www.jaegersports.com

"This book is a must read for any pitcher, parent of a pitcher, or coach that wants to maximize their athletes potential and get to the next level. Dr. McKenzie has done a tremendous job of boiling down a complex topic so you can understand what happens when you throw a baseball."

—Brent Pourciau, www.topvelocity.net

"I have known Chris now for more than 10 years. Throughout that time I have gotten to know him very well. He has become my absolute "go to" physical therapist for my most difficult shoulder problems, as well as for all of my throwing athletes. I cannot recommend to you highly enough Dr. McKenzie's book for throwing athletes. I believe it will become one of the primary resources for parents, coaches and athletes involved with throwing. The information in this book will allow the athlete to not only develop to their highest level, but also keep them healthy along the way."

—George Stollsteimer M.D. Director of Sports Medicine,
St Mary's Orthopedic Group

"With the ever increasing Tommy John surgery epidemic, nobody I have met yet has spent as much time trying to come up with a solution for young pitchers, parents and coaches than Dr Chris McKenzie. Chris explains the problem and provides the answer in a way that parents and coaches can understand and use immediately. Chris has been my go to guy with my clients and goes above and beyond to make sure I understand exactly what he's doing. So if you're worried about pitching arm injuries (we all should be), and how to throw harder or maintain your high performance, you need this book!"

—Darrell Coulter, MLB/ MILB Pitching Consultant.
www.Starttpitching.com

CONTENTS

FREE BONUSES

Grab your FREE BONUSES as a thank you for picking up a copy of this book!

For free bonus items, including a warm up/cool down routine, pocket guides, video demos, book updates, and more, visit . . .

www.UnleashPitchingVelocity.com/bonuses

FOREWORD
Paul Reddick

All too often, pitchers who are looking to add miles per hour, increase performance, or get to the next level end up going to the wrong person *first*. Too many times, struggling pitchers or their parents go to their pitching coach . . . when their pitching coach is probably the last person they should go to. Now, I'm saying this as a pitching coach. The first person I go to when I'm struggling to get my pitchers to break through the next level, throw harder, perform better, or perform without the risk of injury is Dr. Chris McKenzie.

Here's why I know that.

The first thing a pitcher needs is the ability for their body to fully function. Way too often, pitching coaches struggle to get their pitchers to perform the mechanics they're trying to instruct. They struggle to help their pitcher throw as hard as they can and compete as hard as they can.

Why do coaches like me struggle? Quite frankly, because the pitcher's body is not prepared for what we're asking it to do. The pitcher's body may not be healthy enough to do the instruction we're trying to provide them.

Look at it this way.

The Leaning Tower of Pisa, Italy, is a monumental structure that is leaning. As of 2001, it has since been stabilized, but it is still showing its characteristic lean (what tourist draw would it have if the leaning tower was now straight?). If you were one of the engineers first tasked with preventing the tower from falling over, what level of the building would you have tried to fix?

I hope you said the foundation.

Pitchers are just like the leaning tower. When a pitcher is looking to throw harder, improve pitch command, or have better mechanics so they can strike more guys out, they often try to achieve these things by fixing the wrong level.

They go right to the top of the tower.

They enlist the help of pitching gurus, try all kinds of training tools like weighted balls and towel drills. Pitchers and their coaches believe they have found the magic bullet which will help. Initially, it may help, but the tower is still leaning. These drills, tools, and programs are at the top of the tower.

This leads to a situation where players are doing all the things their coaches tell them to do, and they still can't breakthrough. This leads to all kinds of issues.

It can lead to self-esteem issues, frustration, and even depression because rarely does the pitcher ever blame the coach or the instruction—the instruction has to be right!

It can even lead to arm pain, injury, and unmet potential.

This is where a well-trained physical therapist, like Dr. McKenzie, can come in. Dr. McKenzie can look at your pitcher, evaluate your pitcher, and see if there's anything "wrong"—tight, tweaked, injured, weak, fatigued—and he can repair those things. He repairs your foundation, your base, and he literally does this from the ground up.

In this book, you will learn Dr. McKenzie's unique examination system that will get the pitcher into a position where they can actually do the instruction and maximize the potential of that instruction or tool.

Once this happens, you'll have a pitcher who's ready to add miles per hour, take his game to the next level, reduce chance of injury, and increase performance in every way.

When I have a pitcher who's in trouble, Chris is one of the first people I call. I've had him in to speak at our seminars. I've known him for a few years now. I don't think you could have made a better investment than picking up this book. On each and every page of this book, you will find information, tactics, and techniques that will absolutely propel your game to the next level.

I just cannot give a higher endorsement for Dr. McKenzie as a physical therapist, as a baseball mind, but more important, I give him the highest endorsement and recommendation as a human being. He's one of the finest human beings I've ever met, and a guy who totally understands not only the health of the body, and not only the game of baseball, but he also understands the whole athlete. He understands the athlete is a person and the athlete is more than just a baseball player. If you're a dad buying this book, your son is in good hands taking this information because I know it's been carefully assembled for you.

If you're a coach buying this book, this is the information that will make you look like a genius. It will help your team succeed at the highest levels and pitch up to their potential.

If you're a player reading this book, I would suggest that you shut off everything and read every single page of this book. Every page of this book can probably save your career, take your career to the next level, or quite honestly, make your career. Like I said, I can't recommend Dr. Chris McKenzie more, and I give him my highest endorsement.

You've made a great decision in buying this book. Enjoy.

—Paul Reddick

creator 90 MHP Club, author *5-6-7 Baseball Dad.*

WHAT THIS BOOK IS ABOUT
(and WHAT IT'S NOT ABOUT)

Hi, my name is Chris McKenzie, doctor of physical therapy, board certified specialist in sports and orthopedics. I've examined and treated thousands of baseball players, mostly pitchers, over the past 10 years. I wanted to introduce myself and tell you what this book is about (and, more important, what it's not about).

This book is NOT about showing you the latest tool to gain velocity on your pitches—yet the system I'm going to share with you will help you add MORE velocity than you have ever had before.

This book is NOT about pitching with greater command—yet this system will allow you to strike MORE hitters out than any practiced drill or tweak you can make in your delivery process.

If you're currently struggling with low throwing velocity or poor command, you may think you have a mechanical problem. In my experience of working with hundreds of pitchers, I've found poor throwing mechanics, poor command, and low velocity to be symptoms of a much greater problem—a problem that's harder to see for the untrained eye (that's the bad news), but much easier to fix (that's the good news).

A lot of players come to me to correct their throwing pain or to rehab from an injury. But an equal number of players come to me because they have tried the latest and greatest of velocity improvement programs. They have traveled all across the country to attend camps and get personal instruction. They've bought programs to do at home, sent their videos in for mechanical analysis, and their velocity and pitch command still remains poor.

Take Johnny, a 15-year-old right-handed pitcher whose family called my office to find out why he was so inconsistent with his pitching velocity and command. The mechanical problem, as identified by his pitching coach, was lead leg instability.

In other words, Johnny was not consistently landing in the right spot with his stride leg when he threw. When he did, his velocity was up 3-4 mph. But this was basically a Hail-Mary with every attempt—it was left to chance.

"He needs to use his legs more," the dad said, telling me what Johnny's coach had said.

"The coach has tried every drill he can think of; it just hasn't consistently worked."

After I listened to Johnny's story and then examined him, I sat him and his father down and explained that Johnny didn't have a mechanical problem. They both starred at me, eyes wide and with a confused look on each of their faces.

I told them that Johnny has an orthopedic problem which is causing his mechanical "problem." Johnny had an underlying physical constraint that no tool, drill, or any amount of practice was ever going to correct. EVER.

I determined the *unique* primary cause of Johnny's mechanical problem to be a weak hip abductor muscle on his stride leg. He worked with me, getting proper instruction to not only address his weak hip, but other areas, and four weeks later, he no longer had a "mechanical problem," his velocity became consistently 4-5 mph faster, and he now commands ball placement with each throw.

THAT is what this book is about.

Mechanics are of the utmost importance, but if you cannot get into the "proper mechanical positions," there is no reason to keep practicing mechanics. It's literally just like smashing a square peg into a round hole.

Or take Craig, a 22-year-old minor league left-handed pitcher. Like most pitchers at this level, Craig had very good velocity, topping at 92 mph, but he was riding the pine because he lacked command and a process to strike hitters out. At one time a dominant pitcher, a big name recruit, Craig reverted back to the tools he knew so well—weighted balls, long toss, and rope drills. He figured if velocity got him here, he just needed more of it. When you chase velocity, you risk experiencing certain side effects, and Craig started to develop elbow pain, a drop in velocity, and further degradation of his pitch command. Craig was in a tough spot—he couldn't pitch well, and he didn't want to tell his coaches about his elbow pain for fear of losing his job.

Craig reached out to me. I ran him through the BASE-3 System (my pitcher performance examination) and put him on a plan to fix his body's "weak" areas, and, just three weeks later, arm pain throwing bullpens vanished and his velocity returned. I referred him to a specialist to help develop a pitching process, and that next year he was back in the starting rotation. His future is looking much brighter.

The truth is that Craig had "hidden" physical constraints: weaknesses, tightness, and poor control—things that happen just from . . . well, pitching. Traditional pitching coaches tried to fix his problem with pitching tools (ropes, weighted balls, etc.), pitching drills, and throwing bullpens—these things were never going to fix the real problem that was plaguing Craig.

This book will take you on the journey that Johnny and his parents and Craig went through.

There are side effects of pitching: muscles get tight, muscles get weak, and this directly impacts pitching performance and risk of injury. In Section 1, you will gain an understanding of what is actually happening to the body when you throw a baseball—*the side effects of pitching*—so you will understand the basis of how to get the most out of your, or your son/daughter's, God-given potential.

When you understand the side effects of pitching, you'll then understand how you should warm up and cool down. Section 2 will walk you through *how-to* properly warm up and cool down the baseball pitcher to combat the side effects of pitching.

Once you understand the foundation of baseball throwing from a basic biomechanical perspective, in Section 3, I'll dissect the most popular tools and strategies for improving pitching performance. I'll describe the pros for using such devices and programs and also the cons—*the potential side effects*—you could experience by using these. Ninety-five percent of pitchers' bodies aren't in shape to be pitching in the first place, and they often rely on the wrong tools and coaches to aide their performance, instead of looking to themselves and correcting their personal side effects.

In Section 4, I'll walk you through my unique pitcher performance examination, the BASE-3 System. The BASE-3 System will tell the pitcher what side effects he/she is suffering from. I will show you how to perform the same examination I do on pitchers of all ages: on yourself, your own son or daughter, or your athletes. This BASE-3 System will find your hidden and underlying physical constraints so you can be proactive about preventing injury, massively enhance throwing velocity, improve pitching command, and maintain your health . . . from the ground, up. This truly is the foundation. It is your BASE.

After you have implemented the examination and found your "weak" areas, I will show you a plan to correct these issues. This is the MOST important part. What good are examination results if you don't take full action to correct the problems? These side effects don't fix themselves. In truth, they get worse UNLESS they are corrected through a proper corrective strength and conditioning program.

Finally, this process is not just for pitchers. It is for all baseball players, regardless of position. You still need to throw hard from every position on the field, and arguably flat ground throwing is harder on the body than pitching from the mound.

The process that you will learn in this book is applicable to all overhead throwing athletes; baseball, softball, football, volleyball, handball, etc. When you implement the process in this book, it will give you the foundation you need to excel in velocity programs, get the most out of working with specialists around the world, and bring out your maximum potential, while minimizing the risk of injury so you can achieve and maintain your athletic dreams.

That is what this book is about.

WHO THIS BOOK IS FOR

The baseball pitcher looking to gain velocity and improve command.

In order to achieve the kind of velocity and pitch command to propel you to the highest levels, you need to build a solid foundation. This book will show you how to build that foundation and keep the side effects of pitching to a minimum. After this point, you can use your favorite pitching tool to help further propel your potential. This book is meant for players of all ages.

The baseball pitcher who ALREADY has velocity and may or may not be struggling with command.

After every game or practice, your body gets pulled away from its norm; you get tight and become weak—and your body needs to be restored as close to baseline as you can get it. The examination process in this book will tell you what is out-of-whack and guide you back to your healthy foundation so you can keep pitching at the highest levels for years to come.

The baseball player struggling with injury.

This book will finally shed light onto the areas of your body that are holding you back, keeping you injured, and curbing your performance. The BASE-3 System will address many areas that often go unnoticed in traditional rehab programs. I do want to be clear that a self-assessed examination in no way takes the place of an actual in-person examination. Use the BASE-3 System to give you a leg up. Then take your results to a professional who can oversee your program and agree/change your exam results.

Parents/Coaches and Caregivers

This book will arm you with the proper knowledge and strategies that go into developing a high velocity, confident and commanding, healthy pitcher. It will help steer you away from poor instruction and point you toward good coaching. You'll be able to pick out the good and bad advice and coaching when you hear and see it.

Agents

If you or your client know they have more in the tank, they just need a few more MPH, need better pitch command, or need to rehab quickly and correctly from an injury, this book is for you. Give it to your client; it may just save their job, and yours!

INTRODUCTION

The gun fired, and I exploded out of the blocks, right leg, left leg, right leg, left leg, push, push, push. I could sense this was going to be a close 100 meter race. I dug in and drove harder from the ground: push, push, push. I took one more step, and my race was over.

I jumped sky high, landing on my left leg. My face probably looked like I just saw a ghost, and my right hamstring ached with pain. It was my senior year at Souderton Area High School in a suburb just north west of Philadelphia, Pennsylvania. That year, I was flying over hurdles with a goal of getting back to the Track and Field State Championships.

I've always had a lot of speed. The first time I raced someone was my first day at kindergarten. I went to the morning session of kindergarten, and during our break, I was outside on the playground meeting other children. I was, and still am, naturally shy, so I wasn't meeting other children too well, but more just hanging around the other groups of kids.

I specifically hung around these kids who were racing from the double-door entrance of the building to the giant metal swing set about 60 ft. away, and back. This one kid was cleaning up. Everyone he raced, he was crushing. One kid gave him a run for his money, but despite his repeat runs—he must have done 4 of them—he was the champion every time.

My shy self was lurking around the group, trying not to draw any attention, but since I was the only boy left who hadn't been challenged, the champion said, "Hey, do you want to race? I bet I can beat you to the swings and back."

To this day, I've never been shy about backing down from a physical competition, and I guess this was the start of it.

I shrugged replying, "Sure," and I lined up next to the champion, heart pounding, and someone said "Go!"

I was back to the finish line before the champion was even halfway back on the home stretch.

My track and field career went much like that. My junior year at Souderton, I qualified for the State Track and Field Championships for the 300 meter hurdles. I didn't perform as well as I wanted, but I knew I still had a lot of talent and one year left to impress the scouts.

Just because I competed at states, I was receiving much division 1 (D1) and division 2 (D2) university interest. My dream was to compete for a big name school, get big time instruction, and one day run in the Olympics. I knew I had the potential, I just needed some proper instruction and coaching to get there. Performing well at states was my ticket to this coaching and achieving the next step of my dream.

During the third track meet of my senior year, I exploded out of the blocks in the 100 meter dash. As I was pulling ahead around 20 meters in, I felt a little tingle on the back of my right thigh. Then one step later, it came . . .

SNAP!

It felt like something reached into the back of my right thigh, and ripped my hamstring right out, straight up to my buttock.

I was in absolute pain. The hamstring is one of the most painful muscles to just stretch . . . let alone tear! I winced in pain, hobbling to the finish line as onlookers told me to sit down; this was my first major injury—my senior year—I never saw it coming, but I knew my dreams were now in jeopardy.

I worked with our school athletic trainer, who put much focus on regaining the motion and returning strength to my hamstring. About four weeks later, I could begin to run again, but I was still weak and had no cardiovascular endurance. I could finally run hard again at eight weeks after injury, just in time for the district meet. I needed to place in the top two spots at districts if I wanted to get back to states.

I placed seventh.

I never did hear from any of those top D1 schools again. My D1 school dreams were seemingly crushed, and I didn't have the grades, either. Lots of lessons to be learned here.

I eventually made my way to State College, PA and walked on the Penn State University track team . . . . as a senior (remember, poor high school grades . . . and bad timing).

I got my first dose of D1 athletics, and I loved it. I was training hard with the team, attending daily workouts, and losing the 30 lbs. of muscle I had gained over the prior 3 years. Okay, maybe it was some beer and pizza weight! But, I had gotten into body building and truly most of it was muscle. Still I had to cut down. I was too heavy and had a poor strength-to-weight ratio.

After training with the team for 2 months, one day we had a particularly hard indoor workout. I rounded the final curve of the 200 meter indoor track for the fourth time at the Multi-Sports Facility and felt a shot of pain just under my right buttock that stopped me in my tracks.

"[Expletive, expletive, expletive!] How could this be happening?" I said to myself. "It's been so long . . . [expletive], I think it just happened again."

I re-tore the same hamstring.

Again, I worked with the athletic trainer, this time a division 1 trainer. I thought surely she would help me get me better. I put all of my faith into her. She put much focus on regaining my lost motion and strength of that hamstring and nothing else.

In the end, I couldn't run fast anymore. Every time I did, I would feel a tugging and a sharp pain just under my right buttock. I made the decision to quit training with the team and go to graduate, physical therapy school at Drexel University in Philadelphia. Running for a big name school, and now my Olympic track dreams were officially over.

While I was in graduate school, I had some excellent mentors in sports physical therapy. And in a bittersweet moment, I learned the root cause of my recurrent hamstring problems.

I learned that the muscles on the front side of my hips were too tight, and they were placing too much strain or tension on the hamstrings; the muscles on the back side of the hips. It would not have mattered how flexible or strong I got my hamstrings, they were bound to re-tear again and again—and that's precisely what happened. The root cause of my problem was never addressed.

My career in track and field, my happiness, robbed from me before I knew I even had a chance to lose it.

Had I received a total body, sport specific examination, I have no doubt the outcome of my sports career would be drastically different. Someone would have picked up on this.

I am the kind of physical therapist and strength coach I am because I care. I don't want any athlete or any person to fail and not achieve their own greatness because someone either gave up on them from lack of knowledge or couldn't see the problem correctly in the first place. I don't want what happened to me to happen to you or someone you love.

So how does a former track and field guy successfully help baseball pitchers to increase throwing velocity, throw without pain, and consistently strike more hitters out?

One of the reasons I love treating shoulder injuries is because it is one of the hardest joints in the body to return to full function. I've seen other medical professionals be too aggressive when the shoulder needs a tender loving touch. At the same time, I've seen therapists be too soft when the shoulder needs more aggressive treatment.

It really is an artistic dance, and while I don't necessarily consider myself an artist, I would consider myself a skilled sports physical therapist who has an innate ability to know when to push and when to pamper. I certainly owe respect for this ability to many people, too many to list here, and the many peer reviewed journal articles that guide my treatments.

The ability to quickly return a high number of shoulder injuries back to full sports function garnered me some attention with local physicians and strength coaches. It turns out that a lot of baseball players, pitchers specifically, have shoulder pain when throwing. Thus, I began to see many baseball players of all ages and abilities, youth through professional. In the past 10+ years in practice (11 years at the time of writing this book), I've had the pleasure to work with players in just about every major league organization, top division 1 and 2 universities, and many youth players from around the country.

In my first two years in practice, I was relatively new to working with baseball players. Armed with my history of a prior athlete cut down in my prime, I didn't want what happened to me to happen to anyone else—so I dove head first into the baseball and throwing rehab literature, attended baseball conferences, read the sport performance journals, and read what the "gurus" were saying on their websites.

After all this, I was able to see some interesting "things" that no one was talking about. I read articles, studied their data, and came to some different conclusions . . . or further conclusions that hadn't yet been distilled. I'll get to these findings in Section 1 of this book.

Based on a combination of peer reviewed data and my own experience, I developed a baseball pitcher specific total body examination that reveals every "weak area" of the pitcher's body. If these "weak areas" are left uncorrected, they create the perfect environment for poor throwing velocity, reduced pitch command, throwing pain, and eventually injuries that bench you or force you to retire from the sport.

Conversely, from an orthopedic standpoint, when these areas of weakness, tightness, and poor control are 1) found and 2) properly corrected, it provides the most solid foundation and allows the pitcher to *actually* achieve his/her full potential. I'll cover this in Section 4.

- I've examined a minor league pitcher who increased his top end throwing velocity from 92 to 95 mph just 2 weeks after his examination—think about what that is going to do for his resume and his own mental psyche!

- I've examined a 12-year-old pitcher throwing with shoulder pain for 4 weeks that would not go away. Within 1 week of doing his unique exercise routine, he had no more pain and could pitch hard again.
  - I've examined a professional shortstop who failed rehab with another physical therapist after a shoulder labrum surgery. Three weeks after his in-office examination and hands-on treatment, he felt like a completely different person. His pain was gone, and he could perform a throwing motion without hesitation.
  - I've examined a 17 year old who "blew out" his elbow participating in a weighted ball program. When I examined him after the incident, I couldn't help but feel his emotional pain. He asked, "Why did this happen?"

I replied, "If you would have had this exam before you started, you would have learned your throwing shoulder lacked 23 degrees of total rotation, placing you at a 200% increased chance of a season-ending injury. You would have learned your Latissimus Dorsi muscle was too tight, placing more strain on your inner elbow.

"You would have understood your shoulder blade muscles weren't strong enough to control the forces your legs and core were creating, tossing that strain down to your elbow. These and other things are in part why this happened. I'm not saying this injury would have been completely avoidable given your history, but it would have significantly reduced your chance of experiencing it."

This was his senior year, and he was yet to commit to a college. Sound familiar?

These stories are endless, and they cross all age ranges and skill levels. They key to unleashing your full potential as a baseball pitcher is to know what you uniquely need to work on, and then work on it with the best prescribed exercises and hands-on treatment available. All of the players listed above had different things wrong with them. Because they were given a prior cookie-cutter routine to perform, they left untapped velocity on the table, and they experienced pain and injury. It doesn't have to be this way. I know, and that's why I wrote this book.

I'm excited for you to read this book and gain a new understanding of what actually goes into creating a high velocity, high command pitch from an orthopedic and anatomical perspective.

From time to time, I will show literature evidence and/or basically get geeky on you. These sections will be inside a grey box titled 'Geek Out With Me!" and will generally have more technical language and stats. If you're analytical like me, go ahead and read them to gain greater insight. But you surely won't miss any information if you skip over it. The choice is yours.

Section 1
The Side Effects of Pitching

Chapter 1
THE REAL KINETIC CHAIN &
THE BASEBALL PITCH

Since fastball velocity tracking started in 2008, average pitch velocity in major league baseball has steadily increased from around 90 mph to 93 mph at the time of this book's publishing[1]. At camps and showcases all around, you will see scouts holding out their radar guns to check velocity. Coaches at all levels will ask how hard you throw. Friends compete to see who can throw the hardest. All of this sends a very clear message--velocity is important, and you should get more of it.

So much focus has been placed on enhancing throwing velocity that many programs and camps have begun to pop up with their marketing message aimed at just that. Young pitchers and their parents are placing all their bets on getting to the next level from being able to throw harder, and not much else. Older pitchers who get stuck professionally revert back to the same velocity tools that got them there. Becoming a pitcher has taken a back seat to throwing at or above 90 mph. Pitchers and their parents have bought into the throw hard mentality.

But what about having control of your pitches—your command?

I hear it from scouts all the time. . .

"This kid is a good, hard thrower, but he's a terrible pitcher. He has zero process and can't find the plate to save his life."

So how do you marry the two? How can you throw really, really hard, and have excellent command of your pitches?

We first need to analyze how the body moves to answer that question.

The Kinetic Chain

The body moves in a series of sequences to generate ball velocity and command. These sequences start from the ground and go all the way up to the hand. All of these sequences *linked* together are called the kinetic chain.

On the following few pages, I have broken down the kinetic chain into its sequences, or *links*, for simplicity.

In the baseball pitcher looking to throw with more velocity, the ultimate goal is to create tension at key points in the kinetic chain. Creating tension, like pulling back on a rubber band to make it more taunt, will pass force from one link to the next. When this can be done quickly and efficiently, it generates acceleration of that link, which finally ends up on the ball and is measured as pitch velocity.

When any one of these links aren't performing at their best, for any number of reasons (which we'll get to later), links farther down the line take on more tension/ stress and create poor movement patterns, which negatively impacts ball velocity, pitch command, and no surprise here, puts you more at risk of injury. You can only be as strong as your weakest link.

Body Acceleration Links

The body speeds up or accelerates in a stepwise manner to put velocity on the ball. Below you will notice the numbered acceleration links are out of order, skipping a link-number in between (all odd numbers). This has been done on purpose, leaving room for the deceleration links to be inserted, which will be denoted with even numbers. When all the numbers are strung together concurrently in the correct order 1 through 10, this creates acceleration. You cannot have maximum acceleration without proper deceleration.

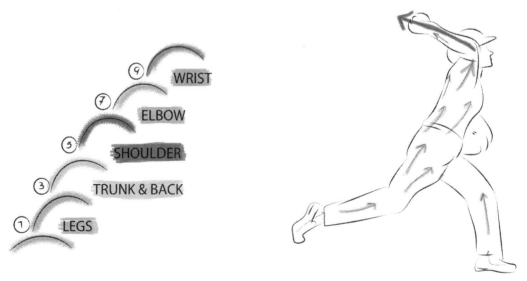

Figure 1.1:   Acceleration Links (odd #'s) of a baseball pitch

Link #1. Force is generated from the ground and the legs accelerate.

When you are standing on the mound and pushing off the rubber, you are doing so with your rear or drive leg. You are generating force from the ground, which causes your legs to accelerate and causes your stride to open.

Your legs are still accelerating until the stride leg or lead leg foot touches the ground.

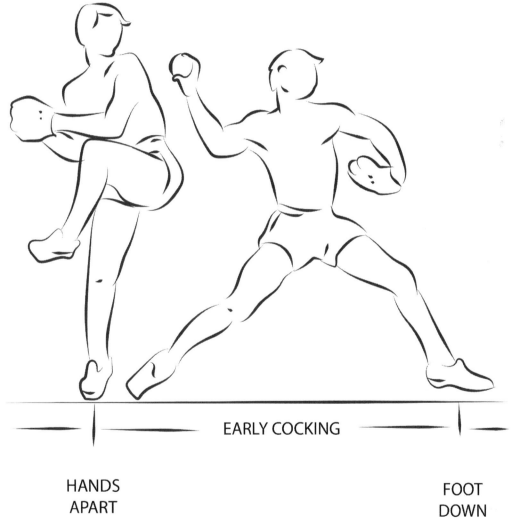

EARLY COCKING

HANDS
APART

FOOT
DOWN

Figure 1.2: Leg drive initiates whole body acceleration.

Link #3. Acceleration is passed through the core.

Just after the stride leg touches the ground, tension is transferred to the mid-section of your body, your core. The core begins to accelerate rotating toward home plate.

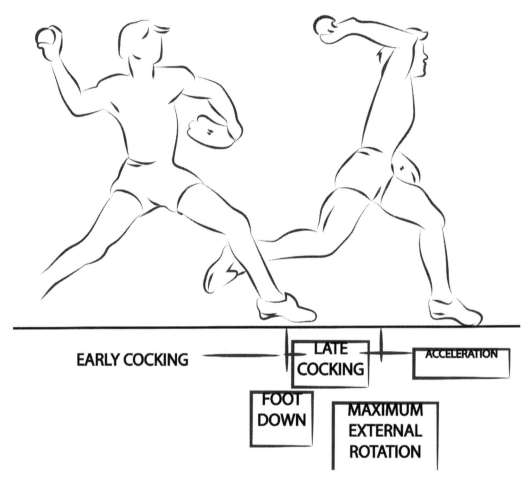

Figure 1.3:   The core accelerates as it rotates toward home plate.

Link #5. The shoulder accelerates.

Once the core is done accelerating, it passes its tension and thus acceleration onto the shoulder. The shoulder accelerates toward home plate by rotating forward from its laid back position to in front of the head.

Figure 1.4:   Shoulder acceleration until the arm passes by the head.

Geek Out With Me. **Leg Strength and Arm Stress.** Kibler and Chandler[2] calculated a 20% decrease in force output from the legs and core, required a 34% increase in rotational shoulder velocity to impart the same force to the hand. This means the arm **is capable** of throwing hard without using much legs and core; the shoulder just needs to move faster. But, this will likely come at a cost—excessive soreness and eventually injury.

Link #7. The elbow accelerates.

Once the shoulder is done accelerating, it passes tension onto a rapidly straightening elbow.

ACCELERATION

Figure 1.5:   Acceleration of the elbow just before it becomes completely straight.

Link #9. The wrist and hand accelerate, unleashing velocity on the ball.

Once the elbow is done accelerating, it passes it on to the wrist and finally out on the ball.

That is how the body moves sequentially in order to create ball velocity. One body part accelerates, then it passes it on to the next body part in line. The amount of acceleration grows over the length of the pitch, with the fastest acceleration occurring as the ball is released. Please refer to figure 1.1 to see it from a birds-eye view.

Body Deceleration

Equally, if not more important than the acceleration links, are the deceleration links.

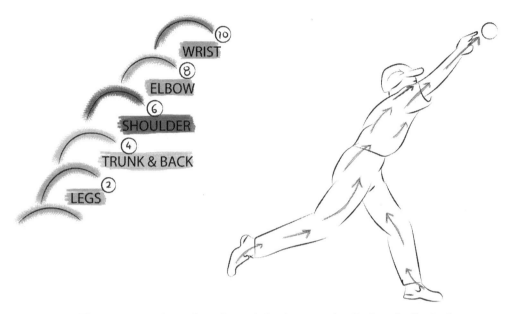

Figure 1.6:   Deceleration Links (even #s) of a baseball pitch.

The truth is, of all the force generated from the ground, you only impart a fraction of that force onto the ball. This is the reason why baseball pitchers should lift weights. Baseball pitchers need to get as strong as they can, so they have a greater potential to put more force onto the ball.

Geek Out With Me! **Fast Twitch Muscle Fibers.** If you are a pitcher who throws hard and does not lift weights, lucky you! You were born with many fast twitch muscle fibers and also have an innate ability to use all of them to the maximum. Cheers! But, I bet there is still more performance pent up inside you. There are two types of fast twitch muscle fibers; Type IIA and Type IIB.

So what happens to all of the remaining force?

It stays in the body, and the body must decelerate or control that force to stop or slow your motion.

I'm often asked, "Why do I want the body to slow down if I'm trying to throw fast?"

Well, for starters, you might need to field the ball if it's hit toward you. If you're out of control, you'll have no chance. And second, you're not running toward home plate after you release the ball, are you? No, you come to a stop.

Deceleration is a natural byproduct of acceleration. For the next body part in the kinetic chain to accelerate, the body part behind it must decelerate. Think of it like passing the torch. The torch bearer hands his flame to someone else to keep going, and his becomes extinguished—his part of the journey has ended, while the next guy in line is just beginning.

Just like the body speeds up in a stepwise manner, the body decelerates in a stepwise manner, too.

Link #2. Stride Leg Deceleration.

As the core begins accelerating, the legs, specifically the stride leg, begins to slow down the lower body. If you look more closely, you will see the stride leg lands with the hip situated in an "open hip" position, and then moves into a "closed hip" position. This will be an important distinction later.

HIPS OPEN   HIPS CLOSED

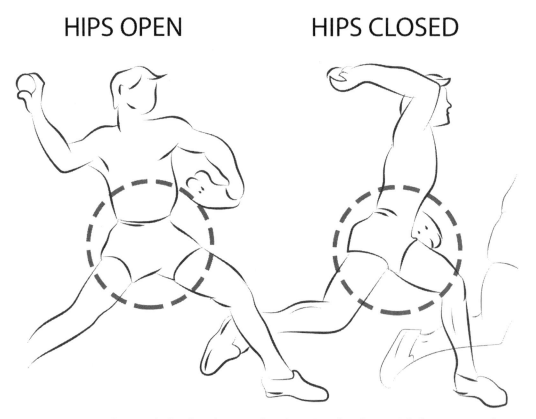

Figure 1.7:   The stride leg hip begins deceleration landing with hips open, then allowing the hips to close. This is where hip and shoulder separation closes down.

Link #4. Core Deceleration.

After the core is done accelerating by rotating toward home plate, tension is passed onto the throwing shoulder for it to begin accelerating. As that is happening, the core, and specifically the back side of the core (your back muscles), begins to decelerate.

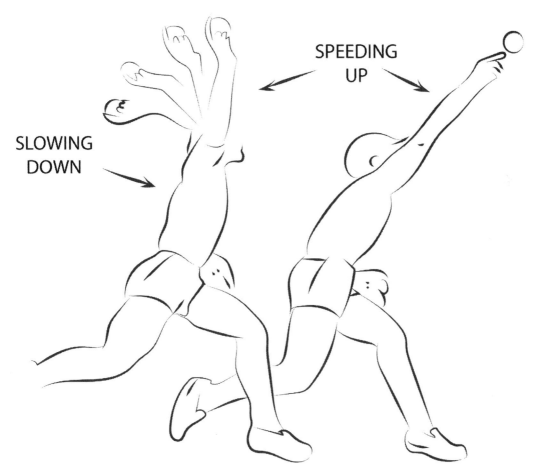

SPEEDING UP

SLOWING DOWN

Figure 1.8: The back side of the pitcher's core is slowing down, while the arm is accelerating.

Looking at a pitcher from behind, ask them to bend over, keeping their knees straight, arms hanging straight down. In more mature pitchers, you will see two areas on the back where muscle is hypertrophied, or enlarged. In a right-hander, you will see the left lower back muscles (lumbar para-spinals), and right upper back muscles (thoracic para-spinals) are larger. Opposite that in a lefty.

You can draw a line connecting the two areas, and this is the line that muscle force is traveling, in a diagonal direction up toward the shoulder. These muscle groups are enlarged because so much muscle force goes through them. Muscles respond to the amount of stress put on them. Thus, muscles will grow in size because of the increased force they have to handle. This is exactly how weight lifting works to grow muscles in size and strength.

If the pitcher has scoliosis—a curvature of the back—or is very well symmetrically developed or under-developed, you may not see this adaptation. So please don't be alarmed if you try this and see something different.

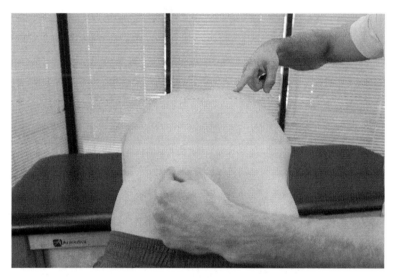

Image 1.1:   These two spots that I'm pointing to represent where muscle is often enlarged or hypertrophied in a right-handed thrower. These areas take on a lot of stress during pitching.

Link #6. Throwing shoulder deceleration.

At this point in time, the throwing shoulder is rapidly rotating toward the front side of the body and home plate. In the medical world, we call this internal rotation. After the arm passes by the ear, the elbow begins to rapidly extend and accelerate.

At this point in time, the shoulder, and specifically the back side of the shoulder, begins to decelerate.

Link #8: Elbow Deceleration.

Just before the elbow gets completely straight, the forearm accelerates. As that is happening, the elbow decelerates.

ACCELERATION

Figure 1.9: The arm has passed by the head where the shoulder has already begun slowing down. Furthermore, the elbow begins to slow down as it reaches nearly completely straight.

Link #10: Wrist Deceleration.

As the ball moves out of the pitcher's hand, the wrist is moving into a flexed or wrist/hand down position and the muscles on the back side of the wrist and forearm begin to decelerate the wrist.

This is how the body is linked sequentially in order to decelerate the forces that remain in the body. As one body part accelerates, the body part right behind it is slowing down. Like acceleration, the slowdown of the body grows over the length of the pitch, with the body experiencing the largest amount of deceleration forces after the ball has been released. Please refer to figure 1.6 to see it from a birds-eye view.

If you lack adequate muscle strength and flexibility to allow the slowdown process to happen in a controlled manner, links further down the chain take on more stress and create injury.

Now that you have an understanding of how the body moves to create ball velocity, in the next chapter we'll discuss what muscles allow this all to happen.

Let's Review:

You have just learned that the body speeds up or accelerates in a sequential manner, and the body also slows down or decelerates in a sequential manner. This occurs through separate links on the body which make up the "kinetic chain." This process lays the foundation for the rest of this book and, ultimately, your performance and injury risk as a baseball pitcher.

Up Next:

Next you're going to learn what muscles and muscle contractions are being used to create acceleration and deceleration. This will give you insight regarding how to effectively train these muscles for increased pitching performance and reducing pitching injuries.

Chapter 2
THE PITCHING MUSCLES

There are 206 bones and 640 muscles in the human body. Every single muscle contracts during the baseball pitch, some much more than others. To a large extent, muscle contraction type will directly influence how you strengthen each of the muscles during training. In this chapter, you will learn where in the kinetic chain these muscles fire and with what type of contraction they are using.

Types of Muscle Contractions

The body is able to move in any way we ask it from specific muscle contractions. There are three types of muscle contractions, and they are:
- Concentric contractions
- Eccentric contractions
- Isometric contractions

Concentric Contraction

A concentric contraction is when a muscle shortens when contracting. Imagine reaching into the fridge and pulling out a gallon of milk. If we reference the bicep, when you pull the milk out of the fridge toward you, the bicep muscle balls up and becomes more visible because it's shortening . . . just like when you flex and kiss your bicep in the mirror!

CONCENTRIC MUSCLE CONTRACTION - THE BICEP
MUSCLE IS <u>SHORTENING</u> WHILE CONTRACTING

Figure 2.1: Concentric contraction: the muscle shortens

Eccentric Contraction

An eccentric contraction is exactly the opposite of a concentric contraction. An eccentric contraction is the lengthening of a muscle while it's still contracting. When you put the milk back in the fridge, it's the bicep that is slowly controlling the decent of that milk. The triceps are not pushing the milk into the fridge, but rather the bicep is slowly allowing the arm to fall to put the milk down. This is the same thing as performing "negatives" in the gym. Such as during a bicep curl, when you slowly lower the weight to the starting position over 10 seconds. That is an eccentric contraction of the biceps (and other elbow flexor muscles).

ECENTRIC MUSCLE CONTRACTION - THE BICEP
MUSCLE IS <u>LENGTHENING</u> WHILE CONTRACTING

Figure 2.2: Eccentric contraction: the muscle lengthens (not stretching) while it's still contracting.

Isometric Contraction

Last, an isometric contraction creates stiffness at a joint. A stiff joint is a joint that does not move. No movement of the joint is occurring because the muscles on both sides of the joint are contracting with equal and opposite directional force. One muscle contraction pulls one way; the other muscle contracts to pull the other way. The goal of an isometric contraction is to transfer tension to help increase *or decrease* force production.

Think of when you land from a jump—why don't you crumble to the ground? Because in an instant in time, there are opposing muscle forces that stop the movement from progressing in any direction. You neither crumble to the ground, nor do you jump upwards again. Your movement stops.

The End Goal: Muscle Contractions Create Tension

These three muscle contractions are what help the body to accelerate and put velocity on the ball. They are also responsible for slowing the body down.

There are series of concentric and eccentric contractions that happen, and in between those are isometric contractions. Like I have mentioned before, the end goal of all those muscle contractions is to create tension. When you create tension through the body, that's how you are able to transfer force from the ground all the way up through the core and then eventually into the ball.

How *much* tension is developed and how *fast* you create that tension over all the links in the kinetic chain determines how much acceleration is imparted on the ball . . . and that directly impacts how fast the ball goes. That creates velocity.

Imagine trying to fling a rubber band across the room. How much harder would it be to get good distance using a dried up, old rubber band compared to a new stiff one? Pulling halfway back on the band compared to really stretching it back before you let it fly?

Go Fast and Slow Down Muscles

To make this really simple to understand, I call concentric muscle contractions the 'Go Fast' muscles and eccentric muscle contractions the 'Slow Down' muscles. But know full well that these muscles must work together to create the 90+ mph ball velocity that you want to achieve.

Geek Out With Me!
The Change or Amortization Phase

Isometric muscle contractions usually happen between the other 2 types of muscle contractions. For example, when you land from a jump with the immediate goal to jump straight up again, you first create an eccentric contraction on the Quadriceps/ front thigh muscles to slow your decent. Since your goal is to jump quickly upwards again, this eccentric contraction must *change* to a concentric contraction of the Quadriceps to produce the action of jumping up.

In the act of changing, the muscle contraction turns to an isometric one. It stops your deceleration (the eccentric contraction) and quickly accelerates you upwards (concentric contraction). This phase of muscle changing is called the amortization phase, or *change* phase. The faster this change-over happens, the faster and more efficiently force will be transferred to the next body part. We call this explosiveness.

In the baseball pitch, for the arm to come forward to release the ball, the shoulder must move from its maximally laid back or externally rotated position, into an internally rotated one. An eccentric contraction allows the arm to drop into external rotation, an isometric contraction stops this motion, and then a concentric contraction pulls the shoulder into internal rotation and across the body to release the ball. This is one of many, many places where this happens.

ACCELERATION

Figure 2.3

Go-Fast Muscles

The main muscle groups that help the pitcher go-fast are:
- Drive leg Quadriceps
- Drive leg glutes
    - Gluteus Maximus & Gluteus Medius muscles
- Drive leg calf muscles
    - Gastrocnemius & Soleus
- Stride leg groin muscles
    - Hip adductor group
- Anterior or Front abdominal/core muscles
- Shoulder internal rotators of the throwing arm
    - Latissimus Dorsi muscle, Teres Major muscle & the Subscapularis muscle
- Triceps of the throwing arm
- Wrist flexors of the throwing arm

Slow Down Muscles

The main muscle groups that slow down the pitcher are:
- Stride leg glutes
    - Gluteus Maximus, small hip external rotators, Gluteus Medius
- Posterior or rear core muscles
- External rotators of the throwing shoulder
    - Supraspinatus, Infraspinatus & Teres Minor muscles
- Biceps and elbow flexors
- Stride leg Hamstrings

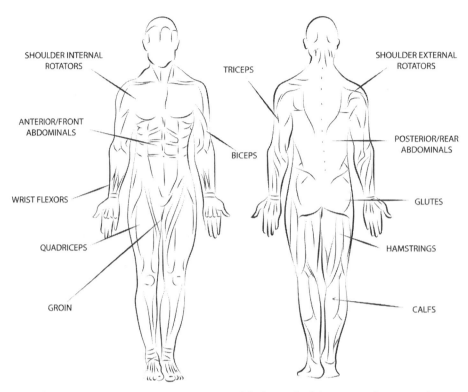

Figure 2.4:   Human anatomy, with key pitching muscles noted.

The Baseball Pitch and Its Muscles

Let's take a look at how these muscles are working on the pitcher.

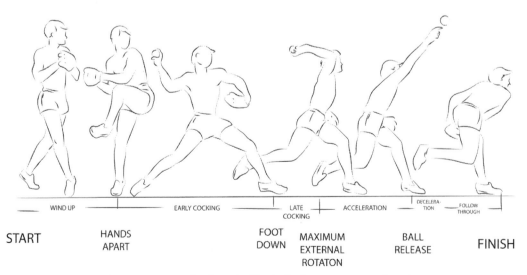

Figure 2.5:   The baseball pitch from start to finish.

During a pitch, after the hands come apart, the rear leg/drive leg Quadriceps muscles, Glutes (Glute Maximus and Glute Medius), and calf muscles (Gastrocnemius and Soleus) contract concentrically to begin accelerating the body toward home plate[3,4].

Figure 2.6:   Concentric contraction of the quads, drive leg glute, and calves. Only the quadriceps can been seen and is highlighted with diagonal lines. Drive leg glute and calf would have the same denotation lines if you could see them.

As soon as the front leg or stride leg touches the ground, the pelvis begins to quickly rotate, accelerating toward home plate. It is important to note that when the stride leg lands, it does so in a hip open or externally rotated position.

HIPS OPEN   HIPS CLOSED

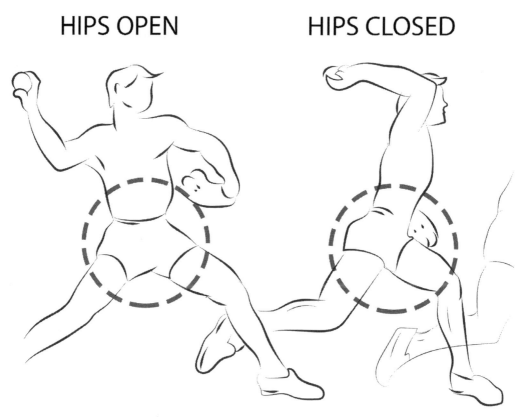

Figure 2.7:   Hip open and hip closed.

The pelvis is pulled by the groin muscles/hip adductors on the stride leg to create a hip closed or internally rotated position[3]. The groin muscles are contracting concentrically. The body's acceleration is now being moved to the core.

As the core is speeding up, our attention must be drawn to the other side of the stride hip. The stride leg Gluteus Maximus[4], Gluteus Medius[3], and small hip external rotator muscles are contracting eccentrically to begin the slow down process. *This is the first major eccentric muscle action during the throw.*

FRONT SIDE   BACK SIDE

Figure 2.8: As the stride leg lands, the groin muscles/hip adductors accelerate the pelvis closed with a concentric contraction (diagonal lines). Just after this, the stride leg glutes contract eccentrically (checkered lines) to begin the deceleration process.

Geek Out With Me! **Stride Leg Ground Reaction Forces Predict Throwing Velocity.** McNally et al[5] looked at ground reaction forces of the legs during baseball pitching in prior high school and collegiate level players. They found maximum stride leg ground reaction force during the arm-cocking phase was the best predictor of ball velocity (even better than drive leg ground reaction force). McNally's study is also supported by the earlier work of MacWilliams et al[6], who also showed that increased leg drive (drive leg) correlated with faster wrist velocity, and thus will contribute to ball velocity. This means the more force the stride leg can produce, the faster you can throw a baseball. How do you get more stride leg force?. . . focus on the drive leg!

The core is now rapidly speeding up from concentric muscle contractions of the anterior core.

Figure 2.9:   Concentric muscle contractions (diagonal lines) on the anterior or front core muscles.

The core's acceleration is then passed to the shoulder, and the core begins to slow down from the eccentric muscle contractions on the back or posterior core. Just like I mentioned earlier, the muscle activity travels diagonally from the stride leg hip side, up toward the throwing arm side (figure 2.10).

Now the shoulder is fully accelerating toward home plate from concentric contractions of the shoulder internal rotators: the Latissimus Dorsi, Teres Major, and Subscapularis muscles[7-10].

When the shoulder is done speeding up, its acceleration is passed onto the elbow, which is rapidly straightening from a concentric contraction of the Triceps[8]. As this is happening, the shoulder is beginning to slow down from eccentric contractions of the rotator cuff on the back side of the shoulder[7-10].

Figure 2.10:   Posterior core is decelerating with eccentric contractions
(checkered lines). Latissimus Dorsi, Teres Major, Subscapularis and
Triceps contracting concentrically.

Geek Out With Me! **The Triceps Don't Do Much of Anything.** Werner et al[11] reported very little Triceps activation while the elbow was straightening. Kinetic energy transferred from the lower extremities and trunk to the arm generate elbow extension velocities of 2300 degrees/second[12]. A concentric Triceps contraction cannot come close to this[8]. Roberts[13] found throwers with paralyzed Triceps could obtain ball velocities >80% of the ball velocities obtained prior to the Triceps being paralyzed. Toyoshima et al.[14] supported this by demonstrating throws with the entire body generated almost 2x the elbow extension velocity, compared with extending the elbow by throwing without any lower extremity, trunk, or shoulder movements. Both authors concluded that during actual throwing, the elbow is swung open like a "whip" due to the contributions from the legs, trunk/core, and shoulder, and less due to a concentric contraction of the Triceps.

Once the elbow is done speeding up, it passes acceleration onto the wrist from concentric contractions of the forearm flexors and pronators.

As this is happening, the elbow is slowing down from an eccentric contraction of the Biceps and the other elbow flexor muscles.

The ball gets released with as much acceleration as the body has passed onto it. Now the stride leg Hamstrings also contract eccentrically to bring the body to a halt.

Figure 2.11:   Wrist flexor/pronators accelerating while contracting concentrically. The Biceps and other elbow flexors and the stride leg Hamstring are contracting eccentrically.

Those are the muscles or muscle groups and their contractions that create a powerful baseball throw.

If these muscles are not strong, you won't be able to create enough tension from link to link to transfer force from the ground to the ball. If you have weak links, you will be left with low pitch velocity. Additionally, the stronger of the weak muscles will be asked to do more to help "pick up the slack." These muscles will be at greater risk of break down, creating injury of that muscle or the joint that it protects.

Let's Review:

In order to throw a baseball, the muscles of the body contract in three different ways: concentric, eccentric, and isometric. A concentric contraction causes shortening of a muscle, which helps the pitcher go fast by creating force. An eccentric contraction is the lengthening of a muscle while it's still contracting and mostly occurs to slow the body down and dissipate force. An isometric contraction creates stiffness at a joint and helps to transfer force from one kinetic chain link to the next. If any of these muscles are weak, they will create a poor contraction and will transfer poor tension from link to link. This means you will not be able to throw hard. It will also cause excess stress on links further down the chain, which will lead to injury. If these muscles are strong in their respective contraction, magical things happen!

Up Next:

Now that you have learned what muscles create tension to impart velocity on the ball, next you will learn what happens to these muscles when they are repetitively used.

For free bonus items including a warm up/cool down routine, pocket guides, video demos, book updates, and more, visit: www.UnleashPitchingVelocity.com/bonuses.

Chapter 3
LOSS OF FLEXIBILITY

Pitching is a repetitive motion. Repetitive muscle contractions and the intensity at which they contract develop tightness in those muscles. When a muscle gets tight, it loses flexibility and its ability to lengthen or stretch out. This will lead to problems. The cure for tight muscles is to stretch. But how do you know what muscles to focus on? In this chapter, you will learn which muscles work the hardest, what links in the kinetic chain are the most affected, and what this does to your pitch command and your body.

Pitching Tightness:

Lots of muscles get tight when throwing, but below are some of the *most important* muscles, which if left uncorrected, will create inconsistent throws, poor velocity, and can lead to injury.

- Stride leg Gluteus Maximus
- Stride leg Hamstrings
- Throwing arm Pectoralis Major and Minor and the shoulder internal rotators (Latissimus Dorsi, Teres Major, Subscapularis)
- Throwing arm posterior rotator cuff and the shoulder external rotators
- Elbow flexors
- Forearm flexors and pronators

To be 1000% percent clear, baseball pitchers lose flexibility because of the repetitive nature of what they do. They use the same muscles, throw after throw, anywhere from 30 to 90+ pitches per game. In addition to volume, tremendously high forces are placed on certain muscles when throwing.

Many peer-reviewed literature sources confirm this, and tightness especially at the shoulder can last up to 3-4 days if not managed appropriately (you'll learn how to do this in Section 3)[15,16,17].

If you went to the gym and did bicep curls over and over again, and you didn't take time to stretch your biceps, eventually you wouldn't be able to straighten your elbows anymore because they would have become so tight. Plus, I bet your topping out at 3x15 repetitions . . . 45 total reps, at a sub-maximum weight. Compare that to some of the percentages below, during throwing that exceeds a maximum muscle contraction . . . and can be over 90 throws per game! That's why muscles get tight.

Geek Out With Me:
Average Percentage of Muscle Force During Pitching

Below are force output data, listed in percentages taken from the work of DiGiovine,[8] Campbell[4] and Yamanouchi.[3] The number listed next to the muscle is the *average* percentage of force the muscle contracts during a baseball pitch, compared to a *maximum* muscle strength test (the kind of test a medical professional would do to test your strength in the office). Scores over 60% are considered "very large" and indicate a very large amount of muscle force is going through that muscle during certain phases of the pitch.

Stride leg Gluteus Maximus	170%
Stride leg Hamstrings	125%
Stride leg Adductors	84%
Throwing arm Latissimus Dorsi muscle	88%
Throwing arm Shoulder Internal Rotators	115%
Throwing arm Shoulder External Rotators	84%
Biceps and Elbow Flexors	44%

How Flexibility or Lack of It Impacts Your Throw

What do you think happens to your ability to make consistent throws as your tight muscles get tighter? Do you think your stride is as long? Are you landing in the same spot? How does that affect your arm path?

Let's look at these one by one.

The Loss of Throwing Arm Internal Rotation

The loss of throwing shoulder internal rotation is more commonly known by the baseball player, coach, and involved parent. Every hear of the Sleeper Stretch? If not, don't worry, I'll get you up to speed. GIRD is a common acronym used for this phenomenon, standing for Glenohumeral Interal Rotation Deficit. Many studies have defined their version of GIRD anywhere from 11 to 20 degrees of loss[18-21].

Since it is very common, I'll start with this example with the hope that it will help you understand why all the other areas get tight.

Shoulder internal rotation in the baseball pitcher is when his/her arm moves *from* the most laid back position behind their head (maximum external rotation) *into* a position after they have released the ball when the arm is moving downward and across the body (follow through).

Figure 3.1:   Maximum shoulder external rotation/lay back to follow through across the body.

The baseball pitcher loses shoulder internal rotation because the external rotators, the posterior rotator cuff, are maximally contracting eccentrically to slow down the shoulder as acceleration is passed onto the elbow.

When the shoulder is being pulled into internal rotation, the arm literally wants to rip out of the socket. It takes an average eccentric muscle force of 300 pounds to slow the arm down. The average major league baseball pitcher weighs approximately 200 pounds. So at the highest levels of the game, the arm is decelerating with more force than the player's own body weight. I would speculate the force levels to be lower in youth players, but I have to imagine the ratio is somewhat the same.

This action happens with every throw. The external rotators get tight with each muscle contraction. When the shoulder external rotators get tight, they limit the opposite: internal rotation.

And don't just think pitchers lose motion. Every player on the field is at risk of losing motion. Injuries and flexibility loss are better documented with pitchers only because their throwing volume is so much greater compared to the position player. But make no mistake, this affects every thrower.

The Loss of Stride Hip Internal Rotation

From earlier, you will recall that when a pitcher begins his wind up, he explodes from his drive leg and lands on his stride leg in a hip open or externally rotated position. From here, the hip/pelvis decelerates toward home plate, creating stride hip internal rotation in order to pass tension and acceleration to speed up the core. See figure 3.2 below.

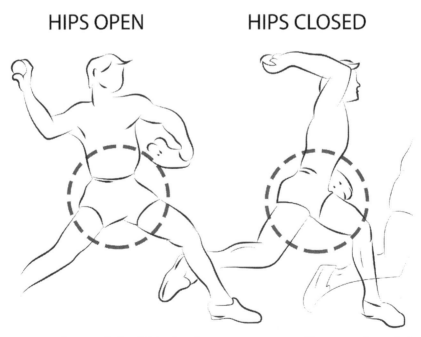

Figure 3.2:   Thrower's lead hip lands open or externally rotated, and then that same lead hip closes down or internally rotates.

The Gluteus Maximus—a hip external rotator, along with the smaller hip external rotators, eccentrically contract to allow the hip to move into internal rotation. Again, this occurs with every throw. With each contraction, the glutes get tighter. The harder you throw, the tighter your stride hip becomes[22]. When the stride hip external rotators get tight, they limit the opposite: internal rotation.

Lost stride leg hip internal rotation is like a 10-car pileup. Imagine that stride hip is the first car in a long line of cars, and your throwing arm and ball are the last car.

The first car (your hip) sees a yellow light quickly turn red and slams on the breaks. The other cars behind aren't paying attention and one after another slam into the back of each car in the line. The last car somehow swerves out of the way and ends up on the road side, averting disaster (for now) but not reaching its intended destination.

If your stride hip internal rotation is tight, it backs everything else up. The links in the kinetic chain that come after the hip, which is just about all of them, take on more stress and strain. This alters your arm path (hear this: alters the repeatability of your pitches), and places stress on muscles and joints that aren't used to experiencing it. This affects youth through professional pitchers alike[23, 25, 26].

Both pitchers and position players are at risk for this to happen, with position players likely more at risk due to running and throwing, creating the need for a larger deceleration force[23,24].

> **Geek Out With Me!** **Loss of Stride Hip Motion Leads to Injuries.** Saito[25] demonstrated that youth pitchers, with an average age of 12 years old, had greater instances of elbow pain when they also showed a loss of stride leg hip internal rotation. Li[26] showed a correlation of less stride hip internal rotation with hip, hamstring, and groin injuries in professional baseball players, both pitchers and position players.

The Loss of Throwing Shoulder External Rotation

You might be thinking, "Wait, we just lost throwing shoulder internal rotation. Now you're telling me we're going to lose external rotation. Are we going to have any motion left to throw a ball?"

And, I'd say, "Hey, you're onto something!"

Shoulder external rotation in the baseball pitcher is when his/her arm moves into the most laid back position behind their head (maximum external rotation).

For the arm to come forward to release the ball, the shoulder must move or change from this position into internal rotation. See figure 3.1.

The arm moves into internal rotation from concentric contractions of the Latissimus Dorsi, Teres Major, and Subscapularis muscles.

Did you notice how I mentioned the word "change" above? These internal rotators slow the arm as it gets into maximum external rotation by contracting eccentrically. Then, in an instant in time, external rotation motion stops (isometric contraction), and then a concentric contraction happens, rotating the shoulder forward.

For the arm to even begin to rotate forward, the internal rotator muscles must contract to overcome the force of 60 lbs, which is driving the arm backwards into external rotation[27]. Imagine five 12-pound bowling balls hanging from the hand when the shoulder is maximally laid back.

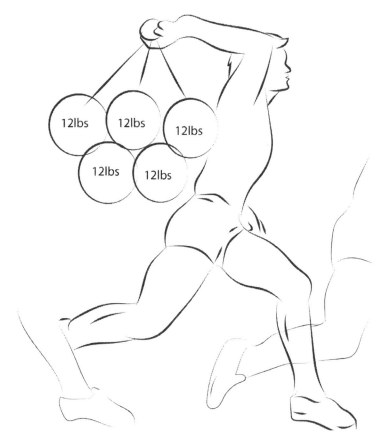

Figure 3.3: In order for the arm to begin accelerating forward, the shoulder and elbow must overcome 60 lbs, that's five 12-lb bowling balls hanging from arm in its most laid back position!

These internal rotation muscles aggressively contract with every single throw, and they become tight. When the internal rotators get tight, they limit the opposite: external rotation. This can lead to big problems in performance and pain if not examined and corrected.

> Geek Out With Me. **Lost External Rotation Leads to Injury.** Wilk et al[30] showed that professional baseball pitchers who lacked 5 degrees or more of shoulder external rotation (when compared to the opposite side) had a 220% increased chance of sustaining a shoulder injury and a 400% chance of requiring shoulder surgery. Why should you care about this if you're not at the professional level yet? Because it's all the years of throwing before they became a professional that is likely to blame.

The Loss of Throwing Arm Elbow Extension

Elbow extension is the straightening of the elbow. Elbow flexion is the bending of the elbow. Initially, elbow extension during a baseball pitch occurs by a concentric contraction of the Triceps muscle. When the elbow passes its tension and acceleration to the wrist and forearm, the elbow begins to slow down from an eccentric contraction of the Biceps and the other elbow flexors.

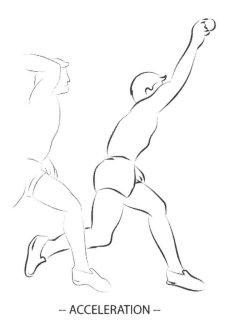

-- ACCELERATION --

Figure 3.4: The elbow just before fully straight, right at ball release.

It is the eccentric contraction of the Biceps and other elbow flexors which, over time, causes the elbow to not go straight anymore. With the elbow straightening at 2300 degrees/second, the elbow flexors have a lot of deceleration to do[12].

Most medical professionals who work with baseball players will tell you this is a normal adaptation. While it is common to see, especially in college-age pitchers and older, it is far from normal.

When I test the "Tommy John" ligament on the inside of the elbow, the preferred test position to get MAXIMUM GAPPING of the joint is keeping the elbow in a bent position. The loss of elbow extension is a common adaptation. A normal finding—no. If left uncorrected, this has the potential to open up the inside elbow joint, stressing the Tommy John ligament or UCL (Ulnar Collateral Ligament)[28].

The Loss of Forearm Supination

Forearm Supination is rotating the forearm upward as if you were holding a cup of soup. The opposite motion is forearm pronation, or turning your palm downward.

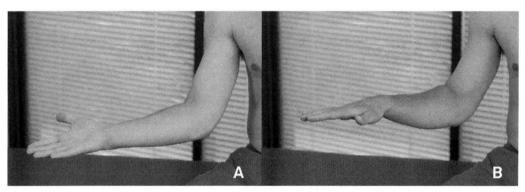

Image 3.1:   **A.** Supinated or palm up hand. **B.** Pronated or palm down hand

During a pitch, after the elbow is just about done straightening, the forearm begins to rotate into a pronated position, turning the palm downward to transfer acceleration onto the ball. This occurs due to a concentric contraction of the wrist/forearm flexor muscles, including the pronator muscles. This occurs with every throw, and over time the Pronator Teres and other flexor muscles get very tight, and they limit the opposite: supination. Supination tightness often goes hand in hand with not being able to straighten the elbow. It should be noted the Bicep is the primary forearm supinator of the arm.

The Loss of Stride Leg Knee Extension

Knee extension, or having the ability to straighten your knee, can be limited by tightness of the calf muscles and the hamstrings which act to flex or bend your knee.

Near the start of the pitch, when the stride leg contacts the ground and the core begins to rotate toward the home plate, the hamstrings and the calf muscles contract eccentrically to continue the slowdown process started by the Gluteus Maximus and the hip external rotators. This eccentric force grows over the length of the pitch, with the greatest force coming after ball release when the hamstrings and calves are really slowing the body down, preventing a face-plant[3-4].

Figure 3.5:   The hamstring and calves of the stride leg contracting eccentrically to slow the body down after ball release.

These muscles are often aided by the drive/rear leg swinging widely around to further help dissipate forces from the body.

Image 3.2:   Leg whip of a right-handed pitcher to help decelerate the body. This is similar to when a Formula-1 or Indy race car breaks apart in an accident to dissipate force.

Throw after throw, these knee flexors contract and become tight. When the knee flexors get tight, they limit the opposite: knee extension.

If the knee cannot become close to straight during the acceleration of a pitch, and worse, gets tighter over time, imagine how this might affect the placement or path of the arm.

If the knee can no longer get straight, the body must compensate to continue moving forward. The most common compensation is further bending of the knee, which lowers the whole body and arm path. This bending of the knee can also happen from poor strength of the quadriceps that cannot contract with enough strength to straighten the knee. Sometimes this pattern exists regardless of strength or flexibility training. If so, this is likely a neuromuscular (mind-to-muscle) problem that could use special training to resolve.

Image 3.3:   Excess knee flexion/bending in the delivery. Not optimal.

The second compensation is a rounding of the entire back.

Let's practice. I want you to sit up straight in your chair and raise your arm straight above your head. Now bend/round your back, and pay attention to what happens at the hand.

It drops.

As the hamstrings or calves get tighter, the arm drops even more, placing more stress on the back muscles and joints, but also changing your arm path and repeatability of your throws.

Let's Review:

Certain muscles must contract to produce or control large forces when throwing. Throwing is also a repetitive motion. Because of these two factors, muscle groups get used, get tight, and limit the flexibility of certain motions (much of which are rotations) in the pitcher. Those tight areas need to be lengthened or eventually they lead to pain and injury and also reductions in velocity and repeatability of your throws.

Up Next:

Now that you have learned what muscles in the kinetic chain get tight, up next is how this actually leads to injury, decreased pitch command, and poor velocity.

Chapter 4
THROWING INJUIRES EXPLAINED
PART 1—TIGHTNESS

Now you know how the baseball pitcher moves. You also know the major muscles or muscle groups that create these movements. And because of how violent and repetitive some of these movements are, key muscles get tight.

It would be ridiculous to link all throwing injuries to tightness, but a lot of the injuries I treat, and a lot of what you'll be later finding in your exams, are tightness related (depending on the age of your pitcher).

Geek Out With Me. **Puberty and Flexibility.** A male pitcher who has reached puberty (approximately 14 years old) will be tighter than a pitcher who has not reached puberty. In fact, if we can level most all boys on the same flexibility playing field, those who have reached puberty are less flexible than those who haven't eclipsed it. This is directly opposite of females who gain flexibility when they reach puberty.

Most youth (approximately age 13 and younger) pitching injuries are due to too much flexibility. Too much flexibility means the joints in the body have too much free range to move. When some muscle or any joint in the body is too loose, that area needs more strength in order to be stabilized for protection.

If you are the parent/coach of a youth pitcher, most tests during the examination that you will learn later in book may be "negative" for tightness, meaning they are not tight. If most of your flexibility tests are negative, there is a good chance your pitcher will benefit most from strengthening exercises for injury prevention and increased pitching performance.

Injuries According to Anatomy

Let's change focus back to those pitchers who have gone through puberty (high school and beyond). This age group of players get tight from how the human body naturally matures. Now compound that with the tightness gained from repetitive throws at or near maximum muscle contractions.

Let's look at some anatomy, and then return to some scenarios listed in the last chapter.

The Shoulder

The shoulder joint looks a lot like a golf ball that sits on a tee. The ball is so much larger than the socket it sits in, and this lack of constraint is why we can move our shoulder more than any other joint in the body. Compare with the hip joint in figure 4.2.

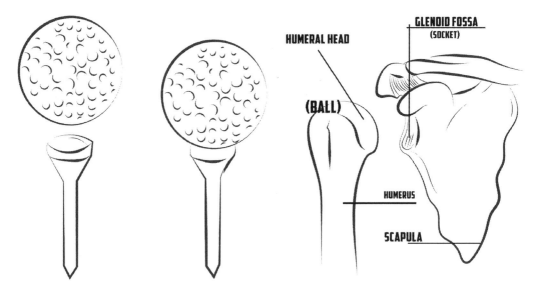

Figure 4.1:   Shoulder ball and socket and its relationship to a golf ball on a tee. Note they both have shallow sockets.

The golf ball can stay resting on its tee because of the small lip that goes all the way around the edge. The shoulder socket also has a lip just like this, called a labrum. The labrum is a ring of cartilage that goes all the way around the socket, keeping the ball stable. The socket is one part of the shoulder blade, or scapula.

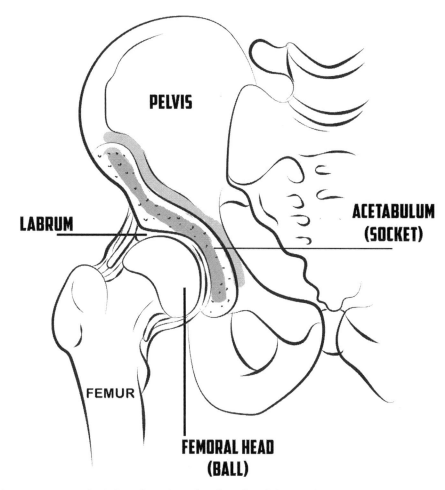

Figure 4.2:   Hip joint showing the depth of the socket in comparison to the shoulder. A portion of the socket is cut away to show the depth, but there is also greater coverage on the front of the ball/Femoral head.

There are four muscles that give stability and control to the shoulder joint that are collectively called the rotator cuff. They arise from the shoulder blade/scapula.

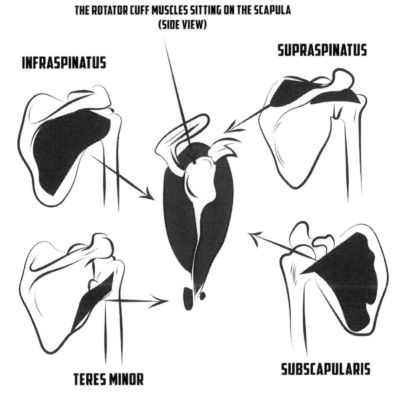

THE ROTATOR CUFF MUSCLES SITTING ON THE SCAPULA
(SIDE VIEW)

INFRASPINATUS

SUPRASPINATUS

TERES MINOR

SUBSCAPULARIS

Figure 4.3:   Rotator cuff muscles on the scapula/shoulder blade.

Geek Out With Me. **SITS**. The rotator cuff muscles create a basic pneumonic, called S.I.T.S. to easily remember the names of each muscle. S- Supraspinatus I- Infraspinatus T- Teres Minor S- Subscapularis

In a study done by Wilk and colleagues[29] in 2014, they showed that just a 5 degree loss of the total rotational range of motion at the shoulder (compared to the opposite side) created a 260% greater risk of serious injury of the throwing arm. A serious injury was defined as "an injury which caused the player to miss practice or games."

In the last chapter, you will remember that you can lose flexibility in both external rotation and internal rotation motion at the throwing shoulder because of violent forces that are created by the contracting muscles, throw after throw.

Throwing shoulder internal rotation is lost because the external rotators get tight. Specifically, when the external rotators get tight, it pulls the ball upward and backward in the socket[31]. Normally, when we lift our arm overhead, there is pure rotation that occurs within the socket because the ball is centered. Now that the ball is sitting higher and toward the back, that pure motion is disrupted; and muscles, ligaments, and tendons on the top of the shoulder get stretched and pinched when we move our arm.

What gets damaged on the top of the shoulder? Really anything that gets pulled out of alignment is at risk. But what I see the most problems with at the shoulder are the Biceps tendon, the labrum, and the attachment of the Supraspinatus muscle.

Any time those tissues are repetitively stressed beyond what they are used to, they begin to break down. On a microscopic level, we can see tiny tears forming. This usually presents itself as tendonitis, such as Biceps tendonitis, rotator cuff tendonitis, labrum tears, or a muscle strain/tear.

I consider tightness to be a weak link—a weakness in flexibility. If this tight link in the kinetic chain is not corrected, the links further down the chain take on more stress. Thus, why elbow injuries can stem from reduced internal rotation of the throwing shoulder[29, 32].

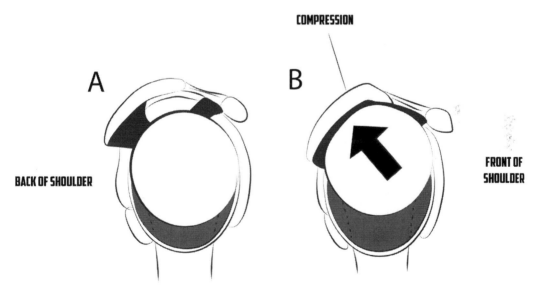

Figure 4.4: Side view of Humeral Head slid upward and backward in the socket, compressing the posterior labrum and rotator cuff against the Acromion process.

Shoulder Impingement

There are structures which sit on top of the ball and socket, but under the flat bony projection of the scapula called the acromion process. The space between the top of the ball and the acromion is called the sub-acromial space, and inside it sit the Biceps tendon, the Supraspinatus tendon of the rotator cuff, and the sub-acromial bursa. If the external rotators are tight and the ball is sitting in the top of the socket, those structures are getting pinched with the acromion. They will get pinched more every time you reach your arm upwards, and eventually it causes pain. As we age, the underside of the acromion can develop bony spurs from all of the stress it has taken on, which further narrows the sub-acromial space and can cause further damage to the structure below it.

Shoulder impingement is actually what it sounds like: a structure in the shoulder is getting pinched or compressed. However, in my opinion, the term shoulder impingement is a junk term because it does not implicate any one tissue or structure as the problem. Shoulder impingement pain usually presents as pain near the top of shoulder which can radiate anywhere down the Deltoid muscle (front, side or back) and into the arm. In particularly bad cases, this pain will cross the elbow in the forearm.

Biceps Tendonitis

The Bicep muscle has two heads or bellies of muscle, a short head and a long head. The tendon of the long head attaches directly into the top of the labrum on most people. If you have posterior shoulder tightness and the ball is seated toward the top of the socket, it stretches the long head of Biceps tendon as it must wrap around the ball (Humeral head) more. Additionally, having this tightness can compress the Biceps tendon upwards against the acromion of the scapula. Biceps tendonitis usually presents itself as pain on the front of the shoulder. It can closely mimic that of Latissimus Dorsi tendonitis and Pectoralis muscle strains and should be differentially diagnosed.

SHOULDER ANATOMY

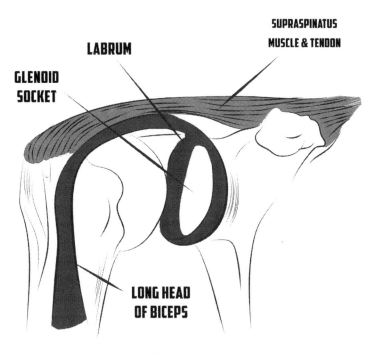

Figure 4.5: Shoulder anatomy. Ball/humeral head has been pulled away from the socket for visualization of structures. The Biceps tendon and labrum are the same color because they join into one another.

Superior Labrum or S.L.A.P. Tears

Closely related to Biceps tendonitis is a tear of the top or superior labrum. If the back of the shoulder is tight, causing the ball to be seated more superior, the ball directly compresses or shears against the superior labrum. In addition, since the Bicep tendon attaches into the superior labrum, all that pulling and compressing of the tendon will create further stress here.

When the shoulder moves into its maximally externally rotated or late cocked position, the Bicep tendon follows. As the ball drags against the labrum, it also peels it backward. Imagine opening up a can of wet cat or dog food. The metal tab you flick upward and pull on represents the Bicep tendon, and the lid is the labrum. This is called a peel-back injury and is thought to be a main reason for how the bicep-labrum complex tears. Originally it was named "S.L.A.P," which stands for Superior Labrum Anterior-to-Posterior, or in more lay terms, top of labrum font-to-back. There are many variations of S.L.A.P. tears today, with the unofficial count somewhere between 5 - 10 last I read.

Another theory in which the superior labrum tears is when the arm is decelerating. Specifically, after the Triceps is done speeding up, the Biceps and other elbow flexors must eccentrically contract to slow the elbow down. This high load of tension on the Bicep muscle pulls on its tendon attachment on the labrum. The repetitive strain of this pulling combined with the peel-back mechanism on the other end is likened by some as a "pulling the weeds" model. How do you tear a tough weed from the ground? You likely rock it back and forth until it loosens up and pops out. I first heard this from Dr. John Conway at ASMI's Injuries in Baseball Course in 2017[33].

It's interesting to note that about 80% of all major league pitchers have some fraying/tearing of their superior labrum[34].

Internal Impingement

With the ball seated more up and back, and the shoulder moving into its externally rotated and late cocked position, this pinches the supraspinatus muscle/tendon against the top, back portion of the labrum. It actually does feel quite like a pinch on the back of the shoulder. I tend to see this more in pitchers who have excessive motion at their shoulder, and even more so in pitchers who have scapular dyskinesis or altered movement of the shoulder blade. We will cover scapular dyskinesis in chapter 14.

The Elbow

In the same study by Wilk[29], he also shows that a loss of ability to raise the arm over head by only 5 degrees created a 280% increase in significant risk of injury of the throwing arm.

One of the reasons you may not be able to lift your arm overhead is because your Latissimus Dorsi and/or Teres Major muscles may be tight. These muscles get tight because they are very powerful internal rotators which help accelerate your arm forward while pitching. Because these muscles internally rotate the shoulder, if they are tight, they also limit external rotation motion. The tightness just so happens to be best visualized looking at overhead motion.

Figure 4.6:   Maximal external rotation at the shoulder

Getting the arm into maximum external rotation, or lay-back, is a goal of pitching. Many studies have shown that a pitcher who has more external rotation can also achieve higher throwing speeds[35-37].

If the pitcher lacks overhead, and thus external, rotation motion at the shoulder, the arm *will still try* to find a way to get into its maximum external rotation. Look at it this way. The shoulder wants to get into its most laid back position, but it can't because of tightness. So, it looks to the next possible joint to complete the job . . . the elbow (and also your thoracic spine or mid-back).

As you look at your own elbow, you can see it does two motions: it bends and it straightens. These are the only two motions the elbow should do!

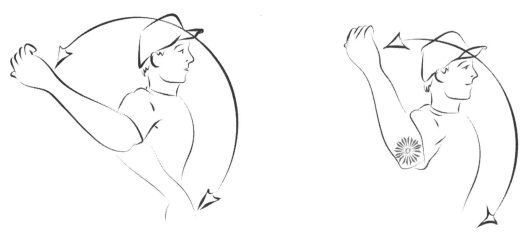

Figure 4.7:   Full external rotation on the left. Limited external rotation on the right with increased stress on medial/inner elbow denoted with a star.

However, during pitching, if the shoulder lacks external rotation, a gapping or spreading apart on the inside of the elbow joint takes place, attempting to achieve greater lay back. The "Tommy John ligament" or UCL (ulnar collateral ligament) is the main ligament on the inside of the elbow that restricts this gapping.

Throw after throw, this ligament gets stretched out. Instead of the elbow only bending and straightening, because of the stretched out ligament, it can now slide side-to-side in very small amounts. This is something we don't want and creates a host of problems, mainly on the inside of the elbow when throwing. Picture a clapper on the inside of a bell, banging against the sides.

Tight muscles can also create injuries on themselves. If a muscle is too tight, it can become strained when it's asked to lengthen. This is often why there are "Lat" and Teres Major strains associated with pitching[45].

BASIC ELBOW ANATOMY

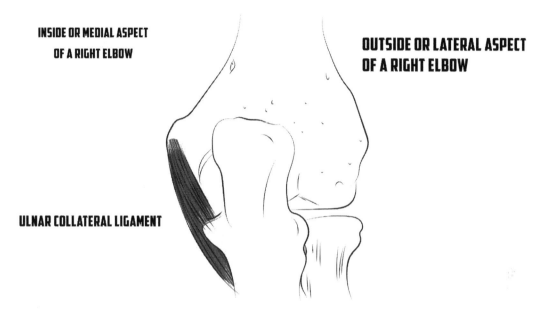

INSIDE OR MEDIAL ASPECT
OF A RIGHT ELBOW

OUTSIDE OR LATERAL ASPECT
OF A RIGHT ELBOW

ULNAR COLLATERAL LIGAMENT

Figure 4.8: Posterior or back view of basic elbow anatomy.

Valgus Extension Overload

When the inner elbow spreads open, this motion is called valgus. As the arm continues forward, the elbow begins to straighten, or extend. Since the elbow can slide side-to-side, there is increased friction and excess load that is now occurring within the elbow joint. This creates joint irritation, like arthritis.

Bones are smart . . . kind of.

Any time there is more stress on bone than there should be, the bone instinctively creates more of itself (more bone) to help protect the area. Smart, right?

Not so! Think back—have you ever seen someone with arthritis in their hands? Remember how thick their finger joints were? And stiff?

This is what begins to occur in the elbow. Excess bone grows on the inside-back of the elbow and can feel like a painful pinch as the elbow extends when throwing a ball. Usually an x-ray can determine how serious this is. If caught early enough, examined, and given the proper treatment (including rest from throwing), that excess bone can resorb like it was almost never there. Ah, the beauty of being young.

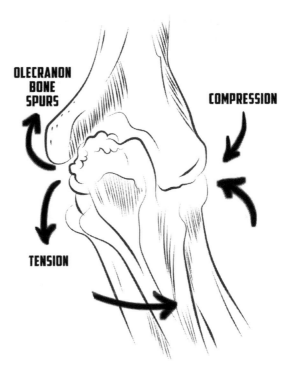

Figure 4.9:   A back/posterior view of a right elbow showing bony overgrowth on the inner elbow (at the Olecranon process) from valgus extension overload.

Osteochondritis Dissecans

Related to valgus extension overload, but occurring less often, are bony or cartilage fragments that can break off inside the joint. If these fragments cause the joint to get stuck or lock up, they need to be surgically removed. If the elbow is opening up on the inside, it's also getting compressed on the outside. Fragments can also develop from here. Pain can be anywhere in the elbow and usually causes the elbow to lock or get stuck; sometimes a little wiggle of the elbow can temporarily shake the fragment out of the way to free up motion. An x-ray can usually diagnose these fragments.

Little Leaguer's Elbow

In pitchers who haven't matured through puberty yet, their bony growth plates still have yet to close. At this age, the ligaments are stronger than the bones. If there is too much gapping stress on the inside of the elbow, the strength of the ligament pulls a small piece of the bone away from the larger bone. This creates pain on the inside of the elbow with throwing. An x-ray can diagnose this problem. Rest from throwing will be needed for 4-6 weeks, but rest alone is not enough—it's never enough.

This issue can also occur at the shoulder of immature pitchers, and is termed "Little Leaguer's Shoulder." In this case, the long bone of the arm pulls away from the ball that goes into the socket because its growth plate is not yet closed.

Like all injuries, to prevent this problem and others from happening again, a total body physical exam will be needed to determine where the root cause is actually stemming from.

Ulnar Neuritis

There is a nerve that runs from higher up in the arm, down across the inner elbow and ends in the hand. This nerve is called the Ulnar nerve. You can press on this nerve if you slide your fingers behind the bump on the inner elbow when your arm is slightly bent.

If you press too hard, you may feel pins and needles in your pinky and ring fingers. This area is also known as your "funny bone."

Ever hit your funny bone? Guess what! It's not the bone you hit—you dinged your nerve!

When pitching, if there is too much gapping on the inner elbow, this nerve gets stretched and irritated. It will create tingling in the fingers just like you hit your funny bone. If any inflammation lingers on the inner elbow, it will not only create pain but will cause the tingling to also linger.

ULNAR NERVE

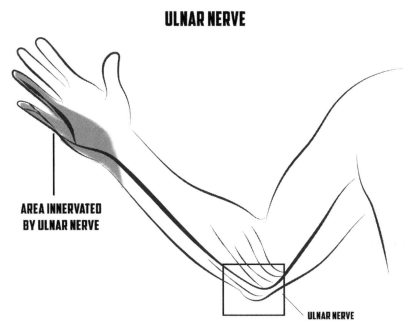

AREA INNERVATED BY ULNAR NERVE

ULNAR NERVE

Figure 4.10:   Ulnar Nerve at the elbow and its distribution in the hand

Tommy John Ligament Tears

There comes a time when the UCL get stretched out one too many times. One of the most devastating injuries is a torn UCL. Tommy John is an American baseball pitcher who became famous for tearing his UCL in 1974 and successfully returning to pitching two years later—the first person to do so. At the time, the uniqueness of his injury and success of his surgery entitled all future ligament tears and surgical procedures of this nature to affix his name to it. Tommy John went on to 288 career victories. With more than 50% of those wins coming after his surgery, here began the myth of the elbow becoming stronger from the surgical procedure.

Geek Out With Me! **Tommy John Failure.** The baseball pitch is the fastest movement in all of sports with the shoulder internally rotating toward home plate at 7500 deg/sec, the same as a car tire spinning at 96 mph. During the pitch, the inner elbow takes on 67Nm (newton-meters . . . approximately 15 pounds) of force to resist the gapping on the inner elbow[37]. Laboratory studies show the UCL takes 54% of the stress to resist opening/gapping of the inside of the elbow joint, bringing the load to 36Nm[38]. We know from cadaver studies that the UCL breaks in half at 32Nm[39]. Thus, the elbow takes on more stress than it can handle with each throw. How is this possible? How can the UCL take on stress beyond its breaking point? That's where the muscles come into play, but they are the last line of defense, likely accounting for less than 20% of stability on the inner elbow, and the rest made up by the bones themselves.

Tommy John injuries have been on the rise lately. More and more often, I hear players and parents becoming tolerant of this injury and surgical procedure, almost treating it like a "rite of passage" to compete at higher levels. They gloat they should be able to throw harder after the surgery, unknowing all along that it's the muscle strength and flexibility the player gains from their post-surgical rehab that gives their arm new life . . . not the surgical procedure itself.

Of the athletes who undergo this surgery, only 86% of position players, 56% of catchers[40], and 83% of pitchers[41] make it back to their pre-injury performance. These studies looked at major league players, but the data for minor league and high school players are similar, but less[42]. For those who try PRP injections (platelet rich plasma—the use of the players own blood elements to stimulate healing), flip a coin to see if it will work. Of those who try to rehabilitate with physical therapy only, only 42% made it back to their pre-injury status after 6 months[43]. The bottom line: the UCL normally gets stressed during pitching on a healthy, flexible body. If the UCL gets too stretched out, it will never tighten up again, and you will be left with a ticking time bomb on the inner elbow.

Tightness and Weakness are Related

Since tightness limits how far a joint can move, it also limits the ability of that joint to dissipate force. Thus, more force is placed on that joint itself, and more force is tossed to the next link in the chain—more force than what it's used to. Furthermore, if that link is weak, strength wise (which we'll discuss in the next chapter), it will break down sooner than it should. Since it is not strong enough to absorb all the force, it will continue to pass excess force down the chain, causing more breakdowns. This is how tightness and weakness are related. One always affects the other.

A player who has tightness and altered movement may feel completely fine until his/her tissues (muscles, tendons, bones, etc.) begin to break down. It may take a few hundred, or even a few thousand, throws to begin to feel some discomfort on the shoulder, elbow, or other area of the body. Every player is different; some break down sooner, and some later, but all break down eventually.

I once heard this quote, "The person who lives the longest is dying the slowest."

Just like we can view a healthy person's life as being the one to age the slowest, we can also look at tissue breakdown in the same way. By *keeping* your body in the proper, healthy shape it needs to throw, you are slowing down the rate of tissue breakdown and thus extending your pitching career.

The injuries presented above surely do not encompass all the injuries that are possible of happening because of tightness, but they are some of the most common to occur in the pitchers I work with.

Let's Review:

Throwing injuries occur, in part, from tightness that is present on the pitcher's body. Tightness in one area directly impacts the force the goes through the next, causing a cascade of tightness in your kinetic chain.

Up Next:

Muscle weakness leads to throwing injuries as much as tightness. In the next chapter, learn how specific muscle weakness leads to a reduction in throwing velocity, poor pitch control, and more injuries.

For free bonus items, including a warm up/cool down routine, pocket guides, video demos, book updates, and more, visit: www.UnleashPitchingVelocity.com/bonuses.

Chapter 5
THROWING INJUIRES EXPLAINED
PART 2—WEAKNESS

There are predictable weaknesses that occur during every age of the baseball pitcher, and they need to be properly corrected or that weakness continues creating a negative chain of events. Many injuries, especially in the youth population, are related to weakness. If you are older, don't think you're getting off scot-free here.

Shoulder injuries are the most commonly reported, and of those, muscle strains of the rotator cuff are the most prominent.

Why Rest is Imperative

The rotator cuff loses strength over the course of a season in baseball pitchers. One might think, *How would I lose strength of my dominant arm the side I use most throughout my day?* In a study of collegiate pitchers, Hibberd showed that as daily pitch counts increased, so did the swelling (or damage) of the Infraspinatus, an external rotator cuff muscle[46]. As a follow up to Hibberd's work, Pexa showed the Infraspinatus remains swollen for at least 2 days on average after one game of collegiate pitching (with at least 25 pitches . . . average was around 60 pitches)[47]. Shoulder internal rotation is also reduced for up to 4 days and returns to normal on the 5th day[46,47]. The study authors lean toward recommending a 5-day rest rule be in place after a pitching outing . . . after just 25 pitches! More work is needed to confidently say this.

Say you pitched the greater part of a game—were you ever asked to pitch again before five days were up? Ever pitch for two teams in the same week? How about attending a showcase after minimal rest from pitching? Ever move from catcher to pitcher, or vice versa, in the same week? Pitched and then maximally long tossed? Used weighted balls then threw a bullpen?

There is enough evidence out there to make the connection that repetitive throwing creates breakdown and weakness of important throwing muscles. Furthermore, if the body is not given enough time to rest, this weakness compounds itself, and the arm gradually gets weaker over the course of the season. Some might call this overuse. But, I'm sure you don't feel overused because you waited three days to throw hard again . . . and you probably felt fine! But that might not be enough time.

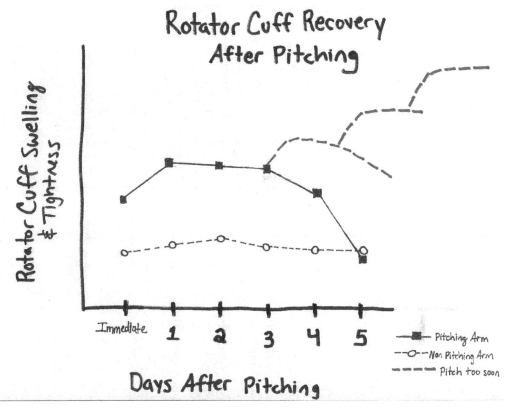

Figure 5.1:   A chart of muscle breakdown with lack of rest. On the fifth day after throwing (in some pitchers) swelling and tightness of shoulder muscles return to baseline. If not enough rest is had, swelling and tightness persist and weakness ensues.

Let's go a bit deeper.

Injuries Through the Ages

Youth Pitchers

The youth population (before puberty, >14 years-old) tends to have less muscle and tendon injuries and more joint injuries because the growth plates are still open. Just like Little Leaguer Elbow, the youth player can also have Little League Shoulder—where the long bone of the upper arm pulls away from the ball that goes into the socket. If the youth pitcher has shoulder pain, it's a good idea to take a trip to the orthopedist's office to get an x-ray to confirm this as the problem. Rest from throwing and a total body examination are necessary to fix this issue and prevent it from happening again.

High School Pitchers

In 2008, Trakis[48] and colleagues reported on 23 pitchers aged 14-17. Twelve pitchers had shoulder pain in the prior season, and 11 did not. Those 12 had significantly lower strength of the scapular muscles and shoulder external rotators, and increased muscle strength into internal rotation. The authors hypothesized the weakened posterior shoulder muscles, which work eccentrically, could not tolerate the stress placed on them by the demands of the strong propulsive, concentrically contracting internal rotators.

Tyler[49], in 2014 studied 101 high school pitchers over 4 years through 4 seasons. There were 19 shoulder and 9 elbow injuries. Major injuries, defined as missing greater than 3 games, were associated with preseason shoulder external rotation weakness.

Collegiate and Professional Pitchers

Last, Byram[50] in 2010, looked at 144 professional baseball pitchers in 1 organization over 5 years. He found 50 pitchers had 70 injuries at the shoulder and elbow. Of the 70 injuries, 28 were treated surgically. The common thread among those treated surgically was preseason weakness of the shoulder external rotators: eccentric muscles.

Sport Specificity Down to the Muscle Contraction

Putting into practice what you learned in earlier chapters, the posterior shoulder muscles are responsible for slowing the shoulder down with an eccentric contraction. These studies point out that the larger and stronger, concentrically moving internal rotators are overpowering the eccentrically contracting external rotators and scapular stabilizers.

It seems like a simple enough problem to solve. Strengthen the posterior shoulder muscles and all should be well. That's what many players, coaches, trainers, and medical professionals think, as well. But it couldn't be further from reality.

Not all strength training is created equal. What I mean by this is you cannot use concentric muscle contractions to strengthen a muscle that works eccentrically when throwing. It just doesn't work as well as you would think.

Jake's Story

Take Jake, for example (Jake is not his real name, but created for patient privacy). In 2015, Jake was a 17-year-old right-handed male pitcher, who also played in the outfield. Jake had made a very hard throw from left field and now he had pain on the front of his shoulder when throwing with 100% effort. He could still throw at sub-maximum efforts without pain. Jake had been attending physical therapy (PT) at another facility for the past 12 weeks, focusing on concentric strength methods for the rotator cuff, scapular muscles, and the core. He had seen little improvement over 12 weeks.

Because of the lack of improvement, an MRI was ordered, which showed a tear in one of the shoulder ligaments. Jake and his family were told that surgery was the best course of action from three different orthopedists. They reached out to me as a last resort, to see if they could avoid the procedure.

It was April 2015, and Jake's mom looked at me with worried, but hopeful, eyes. His dad seemed a bit irritated they were coming to PT yet again, but eager to do anything for his son, this time driving four hours every trip at the recommendation of one of Jake's coaches.

I examined Jake, finding only mild weakness of the shoulder external rotators, along with some other specific areas to work on. For Jake's home program, I gave him a similar exercise that he had already been performing to strengthen the external rotators. I call it the 'Destroyer,' and it's simply a rubber band rotator cuff strength exercise that mimics a throw. BUT! the key with the Destroyer; it's an eccentric strengthening exercise.

Jake left my office and returned one week later. To his and his parents' astonishment, Jake's max effort throwing pain had vanished! Jake kept coming to my facility for hands-on training for a few more weeks, and at 6 months follow up with a phone call, he was throwing over 300 feet without any pain.

So what happened here?

First, the family went against the recommendations of 3 separate orthopedists. Holy crap—I don't think I would've had the courage to do that! Second, they paid around $120 per week for 12 weeks to some other PT facility, AND they still had the guts to try it again . . . this time with me, traveling much farther and paying me even more money. WOW! The things we do for our kids!

Timmy's Story

Twelve-year-old Timmy and his father, Tom, had known me for a few years. They trained at the strength and conditioning facility where my office had been located. Without an appointment, they walked into my office one Friday evening in the late spring of 2016. Timmy had been complaining of shoulder pain for the past two weeks while throwing in the backyard with his dad. Since I was about to leave the office for the weekend, I did a brief screen on Timmy with the intent to do a full examination the following week when there was more time.

Like most 12 year olds, his upper body flexibility was very good, but he showed scapular dyskinesis and global weakness of the shoulders, specifically the external rotators. I gave Timmy the Destroyer exercise, to be performed 3 sets of 15 reps, 1x/day.

Unbeknownst to me at the time, Timmy's father had been battling mild shoulder pain for the past 10 years. He was a former baseball player, who now throwing in the yard with his son, had re-aggravated his old shoulder pain. Tom did the same routine (one exercise, mind you) that I gave to Timmy in that same week until I saw them again for an actual appointment.

The following Friday, both father and son arrived for their appointment and cancelled it on the spot. They showed up to thank me because they both had no more pain when throwing. Tom said, "I haven't felt this great throwing in years, and my son is throwing harder as the game goes on. It's incredible!"

Now, I did not let them cancel their appointment that day--I did fully examine Timmy because it's the proper thing to do. After a few more weeks of visits to work on his other impairments, a follow-up phone call at four months proved Timmy and Tom were pain free with throwing.

In the end, Jake and Timmy . . . and Tom just needed to change the way they strengthened their muscles. I guarantee there was no added strength in the one week they each did my program, but something happened. Something "clicked" for their body because we gave it what it needed. Continued training with a proper sport-specific program allowed them each to thrive.

I can cite many more examples, but the point I want to make is that not all strengthening is created equal. Muscles that work eccentrically during throwing should be strengthened that way.

Sport Specificity for All Body Regions

This is just one body part example. If it works this way at the shoulder, what about the rest of the body? What about all those other muscles that work eccentrically during a throw?

Yes, they need it, too!

As you'll recall, the stride hip lands in an open or an externally rotated position. It then begins to close or move into hip internal rotation as force is passed onto the core. Since the core is now accelerating, the legs begin to slow down starting with the hip external rotators via an eccentric contraction.

Jordan's Story

This past fall, I examined Jordan, a 14-year-old male pitcher whose main complaint coming from his pitching coach was poor stride leg consistency. Jordan said his knee would feel weak and wobble, and his coach told him he could not consistently put his foot down in the same spot.

He had been doing weighted squats and some jumping activities, but nothing had changed his throwing mechanics . . . yet. His examination with me revealed significant weakness of his stride hip external rotator and abductor muscles (and his opposite leg was much stronger).

Since I knew how these muscles work when throwing, I showed him a simple hip external rotator strengthening exercise that put the focus on it with an eccentric contraction. This was a pure weakness, and it took two weeks to see some initial improvements. After four weeks of strengthening, without any addition mechanical adjustments, his lead leg was now landing on point every time, and feeling strong. Velocity increased consistently by four mph. I cannot take all the credit for this, though. His pitching coach ensured he moved correctly—I just gave him what he needed to make that happen.

Not All Strengthening is Created Equal

So, now what?

Well, as the shoulder begins to accelerate, the back or posterior core slows down. As the elbow speeds up, the shoulder decelerates. As the wrist speeds up, the elbow is slowing down. You've heard all this before.

Starting from the ground, if the hip muscles are or become weak, the hip does not decelerate as much force as it could, and more gets tossed up the kinetic chain. The back can begin to break down. Here I usually see muscle strains, or a shifting of the bones of the pelvis. Further up the chain, excessive force will be placed on the scapular muscles. I don't usually see muscle strains here, but since these muscles are getting overused, they get weaker and also tighter. This pulls the scapula out of its natural alignment and causes a condition known as scapular dyskinesis (which we'll cover in chapter 14).

More force is placed on the rotator cuff to decelerate the shoulder. The overuse creates tightness of the external rotator muscles and shoulder internal rotation is lost . . . and like you read earlier, the external rotators get weaker. Both loss of motion and strength here create hosts of problems of the likes which you have already learned about.

If specific strength, whether that's concentric or eccentric, is reduced for the muscle in demand, links further up the kinetic chain will take on more stress and break down sooner. If the shoulder muscles stay damaged for four days, what about the hip muscles? What about the back and remainder of the arm muscles?

The Whole Train

What if these muscle groups were given the proper specific strength from the ground up? Might that reduce the overall damage in the kinetic chain, causing less swelling down the line, allowing you to recover more efficiently and perform better, quicker?

Not all strength training is created equal AND if you're just doing an "arm-only" arm care program . . . you're worrying about the caboose, instead of the whole train.

Let's Review:

Muscle breakdown occurs when pitching, and if you throw again too soon, this breakdown never has a chance to repair itself. This leads to chronic weakness of important kinetic chain links and creates tightness. No matter the type of muscle contraction used when pitching, if weakened, it must be strengthened in that same way. That is sport specificity . . . from the ground up. Expect nothing less out of your strength training programs.

Up Next:

In the next chapter, I'm going to shed light on some specific pitching injury scenarios or circumstances that I've seen in the past 10+ years of practice. I'm also going to share a list of pitching injury risk factors that you should reference often to make sure you're not guilty of doing too many of them.

For free bonus items, including a warm up/cool down routine, pocket guides, video demos, book updates, and more, visit: www.UnleashPitchingVelocity.com/bonuses.

Chapter 6
SPECIFIC PITCHING INJURY AND LOW PERFORMANCE SCENARIOS

Over the years, I've been able to make some observations about injured pitchers and low-performing pitchers. The same injuries happen to most pitchers, but for a small subset, I see recurring themes that cause pain and a reduction in performance.

Pitching Injury and Poor Performance Themes

Puberty

In the last few chapters, I hope you were able to see some of the differences between a pitcher who has *gone* through puberty and one who has not. But have you given any thought to what is actually happening when a pitcher is actively going through puberty?

There's a chance you know of a kid you used to play sports with and, for some reason, they were terrible at it. They just couldn't seem to put it together. They had sloppy, oftentimes slow and uncoordinated movements. The taller kids usually had it worse.

This is what happens when the body is changing so rapidly. When the body goes through puberty, bones grow, muscles tighten (in males), hormones change (increased testosterone), and unfortunately coordination suffers. The body has a hard time learning what to do with its new longer and tighter limbs and an increased ability to create power. Picture a body builder on ice skates. A player's performance can really suffer during puberty. I wonder if this is a reason why the Little League World Series is for kids 12 years old and younger; no puberty equals more consistent movements, which equals better competition.

Injuries in pre-pubescent children have been on the rise. Just today, as I write this, a father contacted me about his 13-year-old son complaining of elbow pain. Upon questioning, his son plays for 3 different teams; he pitches, plays the outfield and third base. All 3 positions require making hard or somewhat long throws. He also plays baseball all year round.

As you'll soon learn, a few of these things his dad just mentioned are baseball injury risk factors. I was watching the 2018 NFL draft highlights on TV one night, and it was mentioned that 29 of the 32 first round draft picks were multisport athletes in high school. It looks like it pays to play multiple sports in high school . . . at least for football.

Fall Ball

Regarding youth and high school baseball, I always see an increase in throwing injures during the fall season. My personal belief is that the player's body has just been maxed out playing in the spring, summer, and now continuing on with fall ball. They have developed specific areas of tightness, without properly addressing it. They have become weaker over the course of two seasons and have not been doing enough to strengthen the body or ensure adequate rest for recovery. My general recommendation is to not play fall ball. Play another sport, or get a proper physical examination, and work on your weak foundational areas with a good strength and conditioning program.

Taller Pitchers

I also see a lot of injuries in taller, thinner pitchers, especially those who have yet to go through puberty. With their longer limbs, they can generate much more force than their joints can handle. Pitchers like this present to my office, and the first thing I do is ask them if they work with a pitching coach they trust.

Regardless of their answer, I recommend they (and all pitchers for that matter) get their throwing mechanics checked. I know that my examination process will pick up any anatomical and orthopedic problem (aside from having medical imaging like x-rays and MRIs), and I know that the exercises and hands-on treatment I prescribe will fix those problems.

If the pitcher is still having throwing pain after all of my treatments (medical imaging is negative for injury), and their mechanics are sound, in the 10+ years that I have been working with pitchers, these guys finally get better with 2 things; a little more time and a very good strength and agility-conditioning program with a special focus on core strength. You need a special strength and conditioning guy on "your team" to make this happen for you.

Pitchers Who aren't Making an Impact

All too often, I see college or professional pitchers who have not been performing as well as they once had. They've gotten to a level of play where talent is a prerequisite and is no longer a strategy. They can no longer just blow fast balls by hitters, and they've begun losing command. Their confidence slumps, and a poor outlook on their career further spirals their performance. Maybe they see a sports psychologist, but eventually, if they don't get the correct help, they end up reverting back to the same old velocity tools that got them to this level in the first place. This leads to over or improper training and body breakdown. The "yips" are more than just mental.

Curve Balls

Current research has not found a correlation between curve ball and injury risk. The highest amounts of force that cross the elbow are with throwing fast balls. This is consistent from youth leagues all the way up to the professionals.

Despite documented low-injury risk, youth and high school aged pitchers throwing a curve ball are associated with up to a 160% increase in arm *pain* while throwing. In the same study, this paled in comparison to a 780% risk of throwing *injury* when pitching while "feeling tired[51]."

Lyman showed an 86% increase risk of elbow pain in youth pitchers who threw sliders[52].

In general, curve balls and sliders should not be attempted until the pitcher can master the fast ball and changeup. Trying to throw curves and sliders before this likely results in poor throwing mechanics, which will lead to pain. The pitcher should also wait until he/she has hit puberty as joint-related pain may be less due to a stronger bone structure.

Know Your Numbers: Pitching Risk Factors

Some of the following statistics come from correlational studies. Basically, these studies looked at who became injured and then tracked what those players had done. These stats have a very high degree of correlation, meaning if one thing is present, the other thing usually happens. Such as if you sit down at a restaurant, there's a pretty good chance you are going to order food.

Other statistics have come from either research studies or longitudinal studies, which looked at baseball pitchers of varying ages, over many seasons.

High School and College-aged Pitchers:

#1. Competitively pitching and/or intense training of pitching greater than 8 months per year increases your risk of having surgery by 500%. It has been recommend that ball players take 2-3 months off from throwing altogether[53].

#2. Throwing more than 80 pitches per game increases your surgical risk by 400%[53].

#3. Any player who pitches more than 100 innings per year places themselves at a 350% increase of having an injury, over their peers who throw less than 100 innings[55]. Any inning you throw in, including showcase events, should be counted toward this maximum.

#4. Pitchers who moved to the catcher position on days not pitching have a 270% increased risk of injury[55].

#5. Irrespective of pitch count, pitching on consecutive days increases risk of arm *pain* by 250%[54].

#6. Throwing above 85 MPH increases surgical risk by 250%. Throwing hard just comes with risk[53].

#7. Pitching when you are **sore** or **fatigued** increases your risk of surgery by 3600%[53].

Risk factors for throwing-related injuries are updated yearly. A good resource for you to check with some regularity is MLB and USA baseball's creation Pitch Smart, which can be found at http://m.mlb.com/pitchsmart/

Let's Review:

Over my 10+ years treating and helping baseball players, I have seen more injuries occur in specific seasons and due to specific body types. Performance suffers in youth baseball and more elite level play, but initially for different reasons. Like known risk factors for heart disease, or any other health problem, there are specific injury risk factors for baseball pitchers which you should be aware of.

Up Next:

Section 1, the Side Effects of Pitching, is complete! Section 2 is going to give you some how-to, specifically, how to warm up and cool down to offset the side effects of pitching.

For free bonus items, including a warm up/cool down routine, pocket guides, video demos, book updates, and more, visit: www.UnleashPitchingVelocity.com/bonuses.

Section 2
How-To

Chapter 7
HOW TO WARM UP

It is generally agreed that athletes should do some sort of warm up before they practice or compete. A formal study looking at warming up and not warming up may be hard to find. I can't imagine many athletes will raise their hand and get stuck in the non-warm up group to see if an injury or decreased performance will happen. Still, we all have "that" friend who claims they never warm up and they feel and perform just fine. I think a warm up is necessary, and if you're not a believer, I hope to turn you into one!

The Warm Up:

The first question you should ask yourself before you warm up is, "Do I have assessed or known areas of tightness?"

After you have gone through the exam at the end of this book and found your tight areas, if any, you will know where to start your warm up.

Steps of warming up:

1. Static Stretching and Soft Tissue Massage (if tightness exists)
2. Dynamic Warm Up (including running)
3. Warm Up Throwing
4. Competitive Throwing

Static Stretching

If you found tight areas, you should perform a static stretch on that area. A static stretch is a mobility technique that most of us are familiar with; you take one part of your body to the extreme of its range of motion and hold it there for a set amount of time. An example of this is bending over, attempting to touch your toes, to stretch out your hamstrings.

This is a very poor way to stretch out the hamstrings, but nonetheless a good example of a static stretch. Static stretching, and variations of it, are the only way to truly lengthen a muscle.

Geek Out With Me! **The Magic? of 3x30 Seconds.** The magic time for static stretches to be effective is 30 seconds. A study[57] in the mid 1990's looked at hamstring muscle lengthening of healthy people after they were given a specific stretching protocols across 4 groups:

- 15 sec 1x/day for 4 weeks
- 30 sec 1x/day for 4 weeks
- 60 sec 1x/day for 4 weeks
- No stretching for 4 weeks (control group)

They found that 15 seconds didn't lengthen the muscle when compared to the control group after 4 weeks. Thirty seconds and 60 seconds were equal in the hamstring length gain. So if 30 seconds works the same as 60 seconds, well, might not as well waste your time holding longer. Since physical therapists often work with tight muscles, we know that 30 seconds is a good thing . . . then more must be better! We usually dole out 3x30 seconds for stretching. Anecdotally, I believe in 3x30 seconds. Everyone can usually get a deeper stretch with more mobility after the 3rd repetition. However, the research does not support this . . . at least at the hamstrings[58].

Muscle Massage

"Soft tissue work" or muscle massage techniques have been around since the very beginning of time. In recent years, these techniques have become branded by industry professionals claiming that their tool or method works best. While I cannot comment on whose method is best, I do know that soft tissue massage, whether it be foam rolling, instrument scraping, or hands-on techniques, can enhance the effectiveness and sometimes take the place of static stretching.

If you have assessed yourself/your pitcher as being tight, you need to take steps to improve the length of that tissue before you progress to the next step of warming up. Since time is usually always of the essence when getting to practice or games, I prescribe at least a 1x30 seconds stretch on your key tight areas. If you have more time, shoot for 3x30 seconds of your tight areas.

In the rare case that you don't have tightness (more predominant in youth/ prepubescent players), I would still recommend gently stretching the commonly tight areas from pitching, 1 time for 30 seconds each. I have prepared a simple document for you as a quick reference for how to warm up properly at www. UnleashPitchingVelocity.com/bonuses

Dynamic Warm Up

Another word for dynamic is *moving:* a moving warm up compared with a static (stationary) stretch. A dynamic warm up prepares the body for how it's about to move. The baseball player, especially the pitcher, moves explosively.

> Geek Out With Me! **Dynamic Warm-Up vs. Static Stretching.** Many studies have compared static stretching to dynamic warming up, and they all have come to the same consensus: those who only statically stretched had significantly reduced force output compared to the dynamic warm-up group[59-62]. Less force output during athletic performances means slower throwing speeds, slower running speeds, poor jump distance, etc. Make sure to get your stretching completed first, then progress to dynamic warm ups.

Dynamic warm ups DO NOT improve flexibility. One study says it does, but I would not hang my hat on it[62]. Therefore, it's important to statically stretch/soft tissue work first (if you're tight) and then progress into a dynamic warm-up[60]. Ideally, we want to increase the length of your muscles first, and then dynamically warm up into that new range of motion that you just created.

A proper baseball dynamic warm up should take all areas of the body through their full, available range of motion, in all the directions it is capable of moving. Picture the shoulder, how it's capable of moving just about anywhere: overhead, behind your head, across your body, up your back, etc. An easy way to dynamically warm up the shoulders is with arm circles, arm swings across your body and then some fast, lightly-resisted band work into the rotations.

Image 7.1:   Arm circles in a continuous 360-degree motion forward,
and then backward.

Image 7.2:   Arm swings across the body and back, lifting arms higher and lower.

The movement of your limbs and, in some cases, your spine should be quick and explosive because this is how we are asking them to move at practice and during games. It is important to always "end" your warm up with a dynamic warm up. In other words, don't finish your warm up with static stretching. An example of dynamic warm up you can do on the field or inside the training facility can be found at www.UnleashPitchingVelocity.com/bonuses

Warm-Up Running

A portion of your dynamic warm ups should be reserved for some running. A pitcher should warm up with short, quick runs, often involving lateral and rotational movements.

It is completely fine to perform a light jog around the edge of the field to get the body moving before you begin your static stretches. This will increase your heart rate, sending more blood flow to your muscles and joints and likely make it easier to statically stretch. I just don't want you to make a training program of running laps around the field, track, or running from foul pole to foul pole multiple times. As a pitcher, this will drain your energy and give you a dead arm.

Pitchers move explosively during a throw. A baseball pitch takes approximately 1 second to complete, and then the next one occurs about 20 seconds later (position players move even less!). This is the rhythm of a baseball pitcher. They explode and rest, explode and rest, etc.

At most, while batting, if the pitcher hits a triple or greater he/she may need to round all the bases. Sprinting around the base paths 1-2x would be a suitable way to get some short running in. Alternatively, a short running program laced with plyometric (jumping) and agility (cutting) drills would be best. After the dynamic warm up and running is complete, you can then start warm-up throwing.

Warm-Up Throwing

Just like you wouldn't jump right into lifting a maximum weight in the gym, resist the urge to make long distance or max effort short throws right out of the gate.

In the weight room, warm-up sets or submaximal lifts are usually performed before training or competition weight. Throwing should be the same. Grab a partner and stand a short distance apart, maybe 30 feet, and begin throwing. Gradually step backwards, away from your partner, as you feel your arm begin to loosen up.

Competitive Throwing

Following your warm-up throwing, you can go right into your throwing programs, drills, or tools: long tossing and pull downs, velocity throwing programs, mechanical drills, weighted balls, etc., or walk up to the mound and compete.

Relief Pitchers

A pitcher who may not get in until near the end of the game, a reliever, needs a more specific warm-up program . . . basically, an extended one.

I advocate that a relief pitcher get warmed up pre-game as if he/she was going to start the game. If you usually long toss to max distance, do that. After talking with Alan Jaeger, he recommends not pulling down (I describe pull downs in chapter 9), as this can begin a cycle of breakdown and cause tightness to come on. Long tossing without pulling down is what Alan refers to as "opening the door, but don't close it." Essentially, stretching out the arm, but not progressing beyond that. As you read earlier, this warm-up long tossing without pull down is probably not breaching the barrier of 25 max effort throws, beyond which has shown to create significant tissue breakdown[46, 47].

Moving along, every 30-60 minutes, relief pitchers should perform an abbreviated version of their warm up all over again:

- Check flexibility and stretch your key tight areas 1-2x for 30 seconds each.
- Dynamically warm up for ¼ or ½ the amount of time for each movement.
- Begin to warm-up throw again, but avoid moving to your maximum distance.

The idea is to keep warm and flexible, but not tire yourself out or start to get tight by warming up too much/too aggressively. You will need to find a balance that works best for you, but hopefully these guidelines offer some help.

Let's Review:

Static stretching and soft tissue mobility work are safe to perform as part of your warm up ONLY if a dynamic warm up is used afterward. Begin with warm-up throwing and progress to your throwing program or compete. Relief pitchers require a special warm-up process to stay warm and ready to pitch at any given time. If you would like an example of how to warm up the pitcher, along with video instruction, and something you can take to the field as a reference, please go to: www.UnleashPitchingVelocity.com/bonuses.

Up Next:

Now that you know how to warm up, let's look at the flip side of the coin: how the baseball pitcher should cool down after throwing workouts and competitions.

Chapter 8
HOW TO COOL DOWN THE PITCHER

As you learned in prior chapters, the body gets pulled "out-of-whack" from throwing. One of the main reasons why pitchers get injured and their performance suffers is due to muscular tightness. After pitching or intense throwing, your muscles are damaged and stay tight for four days as the body is making repairs[46,47]. This four-day tightness process can be reduced to three days if stretching and soft tissue massage are used[16]. Pitching on day zero and throwing a bullpen for your pitching coach on two days rest is not a smart idea. Stretching is a very good idea post throwing.

The Cool Down:

> **Steps of Cooling Down:**
> 1. Static Stretch/Soft tissue techniques
> 2. Eat a well-balanced meal, biasing for protein
> 3. Re-hydrate.

Static Stretching

If you have tight areas after your examination, those areas will likely get tight again, or possibly even tighter. You need to statically stretch or perform soft tissue techniques to those muscles in order to improve that tightness.

We know from the current literature, specifically at the shoulder, the external rotators/posterior cuff get tight and remain that way for four days[46,47]. This can be lessened to three days if static stretching or soft tissue work is performed immediately after throwing has ceased.

Yes, I said this three times now! Make sure you understand this: you are tight for three days after pitching even if you stretch daily for those three days. This likely has to do with tissue breakdown (trauma) and the five-day rule presented earlier. After a throwing workout or competition, make the time to stretch your tight areas at least 2x30 seconds, but shoot for 3x30 seconds before you go home and get busy doing something else.

Nutrition

Nutrition is not within the scope of this book; however, I do recommend eating a semi-balanced diet, biasing for greater protein intake. Proteins are the building blocks of muscle and muscular strength. If your body is lacking the appropriate proteins to repair your broken-down muscles, you become weaker and predispose yourself to injury and poor performance.

My recommendation based on my own personal and anecdotal experience is to intake one gram of protein per pound of your body weight, daily. I only advise this for athletes who are moving through puberty (and older), as the body is actively growing and it's craving the correct nutrition. If your pitcher is younger than this, just rely on a well-balanced diet.

Geek Out With Me! **Maximum Protein Calories.** The maximum calories from protein cannot exceed 35% of your total calories for the day, so says the National Academy of Sciences[63]. If you are looking to gain weight, my advice (I'm not a nutritionist) is to intake 1 gram of protein per pound of bodyweight you wish to weigh. So, if you want to weigh 200 pounds, intake 200g of protein a day. Make sure your total protein calories are sub 35% of all calories, and work your butt off in the gym.

Re-hydrate

Drink lots of water. Our body is made up of greater than 70% water, and during activities like pitching, water is lost via sweat. According to the National Academy of Sciences, Engineering, and Medicine, grown men should drink up to 3.7 liters per day, and grown women 2.7 liters per day[64]. That's about 4 (for men) and 3 (for women) 1-liter Nalgene bottles per day. This will be less for children and adolescents.

Since we are all different, an easy way to remember how much water you should have is if you feel thirsty, you're already dehydrated. Avoid getting to that point and sip on water throughout your day by keeping a bottle handy.

On really hot days, you can use drinks that help replenish your lost electrolytes. If you're eating a well-balanced diet, you should have enough of those electrolytes in your body to just hydrate with water. Avoid drinks with high sugar content.

Alternative Cool-Down Methods

Electrical Stimulation

Motor or muscle level electrical stimulation, also known as "e-stim," has become popular in the baseball community in the past few years. Motor level stimulation is a type of stimulation under the TENS (Transcutaneous Electrical Nerve Stimulation) family. This type of electrical stimulation "works" by artificially producing repetitive submaximal muscle contractions by stimulating the nerve to a particular muscle or group of muscles.

It is believed that this repetitive muscle contraction will bring in fresh new blood, remove any toxins such as lactate or lactic acid, and allow the release of any muscle spasms or adhesions that may have formed as a result of aggressive sport activity. While there is much evidence for motor level electrical stimulation to reduce pain, the other claims mentioned are more difficult to prove.

Geek Out With Me! **Electric Stim Does Work! . . . or Does It?** One study did actually affirm this was happening. Warren tested collegiate pitchers in a simulated five-inning game using electrical stim on the throwing arm, and compared this to an active cool down and a passive cool down between innings[65]. With blood draws between innings, their results were that blood lactate ("toxin") levels were significantly reduced, compared to other forms of between-inning recovery protocols. But the levels of blood lactate were never high enough after the five innings to cause muscle fatigue or reductions in velocity. Some would not consider lactate in the blood a toxin at all[66]. When appropriate training is utilized, lactate can be a good thing for building more mitochondria, which will help muscle be able to produce more force, or for longer periods of time.

These types of devices are found in athletic training rooms and physical therapy offices, and now some companies are even selling their branded unit to the public.

My official recommendation is to try it and see if it helps with your recovery. Do some testing on yourself; workout or do your throwing program and use e-stim afterward. Take stock of how you feel. Then one week later, do the same routine and don't use e-stim. Compare how you feel immediately post workout and the following day to how you felt when you used the e-stim.

If you like it, don't go crazy and use it after every workout. A few years ago, I evaluated a 17-year-old pitcher, who was one of my clients. He was strong and had good mobility, specifically at the shoulder.

Then a month later, he came to me, complaining of pain at the shoulder. I asked him what was going on, and he eventually told me that after every workout, after every time he threw, he was using the an electrical stimulation device on the shoulder because he thought it was going to help his recovery.

We know that throwing is a workout. Your muscles are contracting and getting used. With electrical muscle stimulation, your muscles are also contracting and getting used, just to a lesser intensity. Essentially, this pitcher was over stimulating his shoulder muscles, basically prolonging his workout (AKA not resting, overuse).

Over a couple of weeks, his body wasn't able to rest, recover, or repair itself. When he threw, he was starting to hurt. When I finally examined him again that day, he had very poor external rotation strength at the shoulder.

At my direction, he stopped using the device and stopped throwing for five days. I examined him a two weeks, later and all of his strength had returned.

If you're using an electrical muscle stimulation device, I wouldn't use it more than once, maybe twice, a week at maximum. Furthermore, I would recommend using it only after workouts or games which you deemed were very tough or really taxed your body.

Cryotherapy

Cryotherapy, or ice, is often used to move blood flow away from an area, such as an area that might be swollen or inflamed. Picture what happens after an ankle sprain; the ankle usually blows up full of fluid—the body brings in too much of a good thing and most of it needs to be removed. This would be a good reason to use ice.

After you've had a proper baseball pitcher examination and are taking care of your body with the program that's at the end of this book, there should rarely, if ever, be an ankle-roll type problem that occurs during or as a result of pitching. You may still have soreness which you would call normal.

Accidents do happen, but for the most part, I do not recommended icing unless you are more sore than usual. That would be soreness that is more intense than usual or soreness that lasts longer than usual.

> **Geek Out With Me! C.B.A.N.** If you make the decision to use ice, there are stages that your body part goes through that you should be aware of. The abbreviation for the stages is CBAN.
>   C- cold stage
>   B- burning stage
>   A- aching stage
>   N- numbness stage
>
> The iced body part moves through these stages pretty quickly. A body part usually takes 8-10 minutes to become numb, and once this occurs, maximum benefit has been reached and you can remove the ice.

Cryotherapy chambers are becoming increasingly popular as of the writing of this book. In contrast to using an ice pack, these chambers take it to another level as they cover your whole body with liquid nitrogen vapors going as low as -250 degrees Fahrenheit. This is total body cooling, and some of the touted benefits are inflammation and pain reduction and quicker recovery post workout. The theory is there, but like anything else, you will need to try this to see if it really benefits you.

Cool-Down Running

One of the main reasons why baseball players are directed to run after a game or practice is to get the lactate, or lactic acid, out of their system to help improve recovery. Lactate buildup in the muscle had been thought to create muscle soreness, but this myth has since been busted. Soreness occurs in muscles after a workout from the micro-damage that occurs within the muscle itself. On a microscopic level, you can see bleeding from specific muscle filaments that have broken.

Thus, I don't believe any player should run post game/practice unless it's on their own terms because they have found it to be beneficial for their body.

Lactate, or lactic acid, as it's more commonly known, is a byproduct of using a certain energy system; the anaerobic energy system. This means no oxygen is being used to create energy for movement. Baseball players use this energy system, but they don't use it enough to create a buildup of lactate in the body. Even if they did, the body can naturally rid this "toxin" from the muscles in 1-2 hours, without any extra help from endurance type running.

So if you are worried about lactic acid being stuck in the muscles, don't! If you think running helps you personally, go for a light jog around the perimeter of the field, but don't make a "workout" or testing protocol out of longer runs—if you do, you're just damaging your pitcher.

A few years ago, I had a collegiate pitcher complain of a deadness in his arm in the early spring season. He told me his coach was having the pitchers on his team run 400-meter sprints (one lap around a track) four times, at a pretty quick pace. This was often a twice-weekly occurrence. Somehow, this pitcher was able to finagle his way out of running, and with the same protein nutritional guidance you learned in an earlier chapter, his dead arm resolved. The moral of the story, as I see it, don't do long runs like this—there is no reason for it. Or if you must run, ramp up your dietary intake.

Let's Review:

The only thing you really need to do after throwing is statically stretch, do some soft tissue techniques, eat a well-balanced meal and stay hydrated. Ice is only indicated if you are more sore than usual. Electrical stimulation probably doesn't do that much for you, and there is no need to run to remove lactate from your body. One caveat: If the pitcher him/herself believes that running, ice, or electrical stimulation are benefical to them, and they enjoy how it makes them *feel*, then let them continue use of it, but really monitor how they are performing and begin to physically feel. There is a real benefit to making someone "feel" better, emotionally.

Up Next:

Section 2 is complete. You should now know how to warm up and cool down. Again, if you want a handy-dandy guide, some videos to pull up on your phone or print out to take with you, head to www.UnleashPitchingVelocity.com/bonuses and get your warm up and cool down sheet.

Up next is Section 3. In this section, I will discuss the pros and cons (side effects) of some of the more popular tools and strategies on the market today for gaining velocity, pitch command, and maintaining arm health. Let's get started!

Section 3
The Side Effects of Pitching Tools

Chapter 9
LONG TOSSING AND PULL DOWNS

Long tossing is a type of throwing, and it accomplishes just want it sounds like: long-distance throwing. Alan Jaeger defines it as an, "opening up or calmly stretching out the arm over a period of time to where you can start tapping into your maximum distance."

Pull downs are a type of throw after you have reached your maximum long toss distance. You keep the same throwing intent as if you're throwing your maximum distance, but you move closer toward your partner. After talking to Alan extensively about this topic, I really did gain an appreciation of the art of these throws. As you move inward, your release point becomes lower, but your throwing intent stays the same. Moving from say 300 feet to 60 feet is such a challenge for the arm to control, and this can take many weeks to get right.

Long tossing and pull downs can be used as a warm up. But it can also be used to strengthen and condition the arm. The key is in the variables, or how much and how often you long toss/pull down. However, this presents a problem; currently, we don't know how much and how often one should long toss.

Long Tossing: A Warm Up

Long tossing and pull downs can be used as a warm up. There is no doubting it, a lot of players will tell you their arm usually does "feel better," "feels looser," and "turned-on" after long tossing. But are these claims, especially the feeling "looser" claim, really what's happening to the arm and shoulder?

Staunch believers of long toss will tell you that it opens up the arm and maximally stretches it out. The arm is surely taken to the extremes of motion into external rotation, internal rotation, and cross-body motion. When this happens, the passive restraints of the shoulder—the ligaments, the joint capsule (which is ligament material), and the terminal ranges of motion of the muscle and tendon—get temporarily stretched out, which will give the arm a sensation of feeling looser.

87

Blood flow is also increased in the arm and shoulder. Usually when tissues have a greater blood supply, they feel warmer and more mobile. If your legs feel stiff, sometimes just hopping on the exercise bike and increasing the blood supply to your legs makes them feel more mobile.

The flip side of the coin and its rationale are grounded in what happens to muscles when they are asked to make maximum effort long throws. When you make maximum effort throws, maximum effort muscle contractions are utilized. Using what you learned from earlier in this book, would you expect high force muscle contractions to make you tighter or more flexible?

I do not disagree that arms generally "feel better" after long tossing, but the rationale for why this occurs is unclear. In addition, "feel better" might mean one thing to you and something different for another guy.

As a former multisport athlete, I can tell you of the advantages of maximally warming up, whether that be running maximum speed sprints to warm up for track, or getting into a full speed collision with a blocking dummy for football. It just feels good to go game speed before the actual game. You feel "turned-on" and ready to go. I believe that also does something to your psyche and mental readiness.

But, let's dig into this a bit more.

Long Tossing: A Tool for Strengthening

What may seem like opposing views listed above, to me this means that long tossing can be used for multiple training purposes. Long tossing (the max distance efforts) and pull downs are forms of arm strengthening and conditioning; just like max effort weight lifting, max effort throws are the same.

Alan Jaeger suggests working out to max distance, staying there for just a few throws, and then (if you have conditioned enough) pulling down moving approximately 10 feet closer to your partner with each throw. Jaeger recommends that players don't start pulling down for the first two or three weeks of getting their arm into distance shape. Once your *max distance* is achieved comfortably (you're using *max effort* to get here), then you can begin the pull down phase of long tossing.

Each pull down throw is a maximum effort throw. If you long tossed out to 300 feet and pulled down back to 60 feet, that's potentially up to 24 maximum effort throws. That would be in addition to the sub-maximal throws it took to get out there and the 2-5 throws at your maximum long toss distance. Adding all that up could be pushing close to 35-40 near or at maximum effort throws. I consider 40 total throws to be low-to-mid volume in the mature pitcher, but it's still 40 high intense throws.

At the high school level and progressing to the professional level (weird how a 14 year old and a 23+ year old can be classified in the same group), 100 pitches thrown is often considered by many to be the cutoff for when to pull a pitcher. Therefore, 40 maximum effort throws is pretty close to half of your workload on the mound. Is it safe for the mature pitcher to perform 40 maximum effort throws, not count them toward their pitch count, and then throw in the game starting with a pitch count of zero?

However, I would ask the pitcher how he feels after long tossing—more fatigued after a few innings or more alive? Keep tabs on this feeling during later innings, too. Since the body does give us clues, that could be your answer—the trick is learning to listen to your body. For those who subscribe to a "feel method," this will likely work for you. For those who need more hard numbers, on the following pages I'll present a more objective way to keep you informed of your arm's health and potential danger for injury.

Furthermore, I don't think many 13 year olds are throwing out to 300 feet, so total maximum effort throws will be less. If 7-10 year olds are throwing their maximum effort while pitching, you could make the argument that they, too, should be long tossing/pulling down. How far their long toss distance gets and how many pull downs they make is very individualistic.

Geek Out With Me! **Humeral Retroversion.** When humans are born, the upper arm bone, or Humerus, is naturally twisted backwards, giving us lots of shoulder external rotation. The Humerus then undergoes a natural de-rotation process, where we lose external rotation motion, and 80% of this is complete by age 8[68]. Throwing stops this de-rotation process, and having larger amounts of humeral retroversion is seen as a positive adaptation via 1) a gain in external rotation without the stress on the shoulder, and 2) more external rotation is correlated with greater velocity. However, studies of professional pitches have shown that while there are less injuries on the shoulder due to humeral retroversion, there are increased injuries at the elbow[69]. This creates an interesting dichotomy: If you throw *too much* when your growth plates are open, you place too much stress on the arm and increase your chance of injury. If you don't throw *enough* when your growth plates are open, you won't apply enough stress to develop an ability to throw hard when you are older. Some food for thought.

Long Toss Dosing

Similarities to weight room strength training

Jaeger suggests daily long tossing but, most important, listening to your arm and learning to understand how it feels. Simply, if it doesn't feel right or the arm isn't loosening up, stop and live to throw another day. When I compare Jaeger's long toss method to maximum effort strength programming, I can see similarities. With max effort strength training, daily repetition volume is kept low, but weekly repetition volume is higher. Basically, you can strength train the same muscle daily because even though the weight lifted is very heavy, you aren't lifting it for many reps. This causes almost no soreness, which allows you to train again the following day, and the day after that . . . adding up the weekly training volume, and that's where the strength gains are made. Thus, it's not a stretch to think that lower throwing volume at higher intensities can be done on a daily basis, too.

Arm Stress

There have been a few studies looking at arm stress with long tossing compared to mound pitching. Dr. Glenn Fleisig, a researcher for the American Sports Medicine Institute (ASMI), found that collegiate pitchers throwing at 120 feet produced similar stress to that of pitching from a mound. Throwing at 180 feet created greater stress on the arm than pitching off a mound, and throwing at a player's maximum distance (average distance was 264 feet) increased stress on the arm by 10%[70]. Ten percent doesn't seem like a lot, but it's a pretty good rate of return for us lay-folk in the stock market! Also, who knows what happens after 264 feet! Does stress stay the same? Increase? More research is needed.

Slenker[71] and fellow researchers found similar, but not equivalent, results. In collegiate pitchers, they found no force differences on the shoulder or elbow between flat ground throws at 60 to 180 feet and mound pitching. Said another way, throwing at 60 feet through 180 feet is as intense on the shoulder and elbow as pitching off a mound. This study did not look at maximum distance throwing. Neither study looked at youth athletes.

Perceived Effort

Interestingly, in Slenker's study, when pitchers threw at 60% of perceived effort from the mound, they actually generated shoulder and elbow forces of 76% and ball speeds approaching 85% of maximum[71]. Therefore, it may not be a stretch to say that throws perceived to be at 80% come close to 100% of max effort forces and ball speeds.

Adding Long Tosses to Pitch Counts

If there are pitch count limits for maximum effort throws from the mound, and if long tossing is as stressful, if not more stressful, than pitching on the mound, wouldn't it make sense to include at least a portion of your long toss throws in your total pitch limit for the day and week? If pitch count guidelines limit successive days of pitching, it would be smart to limit your longer toss throws, as well.

At the time of the writing of this book, there is not enough research telling us what amount or intensity of throwing is healthy and what is unhealthy. Pitch counts have reportedly been shown to reduce arm injuries by 50% in Little League[72] and also later in life as a professional[73]. However, increased stress on the arm is not a bad thing—this is how the arm gets stronger, after all. But at what intensity or volume of stress should we stop is unclear right now.

If, at this point in time, it were up to me to make a broad, sweeping decision on long tossing volume and distance, I could not. Just like what you will learn about yourself in the coming examination, each player is different and requires different programming. I know guys who love to long toss, and I also know guys who dislike it. A youth player will not touch near the distances of a major leaguer, and that should not be their goal.

Youth Pitcher Long Toss Dosing

If a 12-year-old pitcher works his/her way out to throwing 150 feet as their maximum distance, throws 5 throws there, and perceived the prior 10 throws were at 80% of their max effort, I would make the argument that 15 throws of this athlete's pitch count be accounted for. Using the current pitch guidelines set by Major League Baseball and USA Baseball and found at http://m.mlb.com/pitchsmart/pitching-guidelines/[74], this pitcher will have 70 daily pitches left. If this same 12 year old were to begin a pull down phase (max effort throws, moving inward 10 feet per throw to 50 feet), that will take 10 more throws off the pitch count for the day, leaving him/her with 60 throws remaining.

Mature Pitcher Long-Toss Dosing

If a 17 year old works his/her way out to 300 feet maximum distance, takes 5 throws there, perceives the past 7 throws as 80% effort, and pulls down to 60 feet (24 throws moving inward 10ft/throw), they should take 36 throws off of their pitch count, leaving them with 69 pitches remaining.

A New Formula for Long-Toss Dosing

You can use this simple formula, along with the pitch count limits, to guide your arm health:

# of throws perceived to be at 80% + # of throws at maximum distance + # of pull down throws = # of pitches to subtract from your total pitch count.

# of throws perceived to be at 80%	+	# of throws at maximum distance	+	# of pull down throws	=	# of pitches to subtract from your daily pitch count maximum

Pitch Count Guidelines for 2018

Age	Daily Max Pitches in a Game	Required Rest (Pitches)					
		0 days	1 days	2 days	3 days	4 days	5 days
7-8	50	1-20	21-35	36-50	n/a	n/a	n/a
9-10	75	1-20	21-35	36-50	51-65	66+	n/a
11-12	85	1-20	21-35	36-50	51-65	66+	n/a
13-14	95	1-20	21-35	36-50	51-65	66+	n/a
15-16	95	1-30	31-45	46-60	61-75	76+	n/a
17-18	105	1-30	31-45	46-60	61-80	81+	n/a
19-22	120	1-30	31-45	46-60	61-80	81-105	106+

Re-created from http://m.mlb.com/pitchsmart/pitching-guidelines/

The Side Effects of Long Tossing

The Negatives

Long tossing takes the joints of the arm (but probably the whole body) into its extremes of range of motion. It also uses maximum muscle contractions when throwing at or near your longest distance, and again with pull downs. If you don't have all the range of motion you need, the arm is sure to be forcibly pushed or pulled into these new, end ranges.

If you don't have the strength in your body to control these forces, muscles and tendons or the passive restraints (bone, cartilage, ligament) will take on more stress and could break down sooner. This can be traumatic for the body and can lead to arm pain and injury, especially if little regard is given to how the body is feeling . . . which most athletes are "great" at . . . catch the sarcasm? Injuries don't happen . . . until they do. You began long tossing because you wanted to increase your performance, but poor pitch command and reduced velocity ensues because of increased soreness and pain.

The Positives

I like long toss because it challenges the arm. It puts the arm in spaces and under higher loads that it doesn't usually see when pitching. *Usually* is the key word here and greatly depends on the age of the player and distance thrown. Body muscles, including the arm, fatigue, and joint and tendon stress increase. If the body is experiencing these elevated stress levels for the first time, there is a greater chance of injury since it will likely be occurring in a non-controlled environment with lots of adrenalin (a game).

Compare that with gradually stressing the arm in a controlled environment, where the intent is to listen to and feel how the arm is responding, and sprinkling in some objectivity. You can think of long tossing like balance training. To improve your balance, you train in positions that challenge your balance: eyes closed, standing on unstable surfaces, on one leg, balancing an egg on your head, etc. The more you practice these crazy positions, the greater your balance becomes not only in those positions, but standing still when sudden challenges to your balance are experienced.

If you want more info on long tossing and pull downs, I had a great conversation with Alan that I've posted in the Unleash Your Pitching Velocity member community on Facebook. We talked about so much that I couldn't drop into the book, but it's definitely valuable and information that you can implement today. I'll tell you how to access this group at the end of the book. Alan also has a great guide for sale called "Year Round Throwing," which you can find at: www. UnleashPitchingVelocity.com/bonuses.

Let's Review:

Long tossing and pull downs can be used as a strengthening tool and as a warm-up tool. Long tossing will increase stress on your body, including the arm, and it uses maximal muscle contractions to do so. This can make the arm feel looser but, in the end, will cause the arm to get tighter, just like all forms of throwing. In a controlled environment, and with respect to pitch counts, long tossing and pull downs are likely a safe technique when you listen to your body. I strongly believe you need a proper throwing specific physical examination before you begin long tossing (you'll learn this in the next section), as you may already be tight . . . or weak. The act of maximum effort throwing could lead to undesired soreness or injury on top of your tightness and weakness.

Up Next:

One of the most popular tools right now to increase velocity is with over and underweighted ball training. In the next chapter, I'll walk you through weighted ball training, how it is claimed to work, and how it actually works, so you can make the decision if it is right for you.

Chapter 10
WEIGHTED BALL TRAINING

A standard baseball weighs five ounces. Weighted ball training is a program that uses baseballs that weigh more AND less than a standard baseball. This type of training is often used in the offseason to help condition the arm.

The goals of using these over and underweighted balls is to improve throwing mechanics and improve velocity and command by improving the fitness of the arm.

Fitness must be defined by the task one is trying to complete. The kind of fitness someone needs to be a firefighter is different from a baseball player, which is different from a hotdog eating champion. Arm fitness, with regard to the baseball pitcher, must include having adequate arm flexibility, strength, stability, power, speed, control, and resiliency. Therefore, if weighted ball training is to improve arm fitness, it must at have an impact on at least some of these.

Weighted Balls in Laboratory Research

In laboratory testing[75], the lighter the ball thrown, the faster the ball moves. The heavier the ball thrown, the slower the ball moves. This makes sense to me, as I can see the difference between trying to throw a shot-put and a clementine fruit. Drastic I know, but hopefully it paints a picture for you, too.

Lighter ball throws (four ounces) are associated with *the same arm speeds* and same arm forces as throwing a standard ball. Heavier balls actually create less force on the arm, compared to throwing a standard ball. In a lab setting, using a four-ounce ball, arm speed is not increased beyond what already occurs with a standard five-ounce ball. Thus, in a lab setting, no changes in pitch mechanics are seen.

Weighted Balls in Clinic Research

Outside of the lab, Drs. Mike Reinold and Lenny Marcrina, fellow physical therapists at Champion Physical Therapy and Performance just outside of Boston, along with researchers at ASMI, designed a 6-week study using an actual weighted ball training program and throwing-specific strength and conditioning. They followed 38 high school players aged 13-18 years old over 1 season. Players were split into 2 groups: a weighted ball training group, and a control group/ no weighted ball training. Both groups participated in the same strength and conditioning programs[76].

Baseline Measurements

Using a device called a Motus sleeve, and together with their examination skills, they recorded baseline measurements in:
- Shoulder and elbow range of motion
- Shoulder strength
- Arm Speed
- Ball Speed/Velocity

These items, along with injuries, were also re-measured at the end of the six-week training program. Here is what they found:

Ball Velocity

The weighted ball group showed an average 3% increase of 2.2 mph (from 67-to-69mph). The control group did not show a *significant* increase in ball velocity. When looking a little closer, 80% of the weighted group showed an increase in velocity, while 12% showed a *decrease* in velocity.

Sixty-seven percent of the control group also showed an increase in velocity, and 14% showed a decrease.

As Mike notes, weighted ball training does help increase velocity in some, but in others it is lessened. The same can be said for not throwing weighted balls.

Shoulder Range of Motion

The weighted ball group showed a significant increase of five degrees (average) of external rotation range of motion after the six-week training, where the control group did not. Six weeks might be too fast to forcibly gain that much range of motion, but it's not known at this time. Since greater shoulder external rotation is associated with faster pitching velocities, this could be the reason for the velocity gains seen by the weighted group. A gain in external rotation has also been correlated with increased shoulder and elbow forces.

Shoulder Strength

Shoulder external rotation strength increased by 13% in the *control* group. Despite focused efforts through strength and conditioning to improve shoulder external rotation strength in both groups, the weighted group showed no change. This is concerning, because it seems as though weighted ball training resists positive change in strength. It could be that the addition of weighted ball throwing combined with throwing specific strength and conditioning caused more fatigue, which caused the rotator cuff to test weaker. Regardless, this lack of strength gain from throwing alone is consistent with other studies[44].

Perhaps this result would have changed if different rest periods were used for strength training or throwing. Maybe even not strength training while doing weighted balls . . .? Unfortunately, we do not know what is optimal yet, and more studies are needed.

As of right now, arm strength does not improve and furthermore does not appear to aid the velocity gains seen after a six-week weighted ball program.

Arm Speed and Elbow Stress

Elbow stress and arm speed were not different following six weeks of training in either group. Thus, we cannot say that weighted ball training increases pitch velocity by improving arm speed.

Injuries

Zero injuries were reported in the control group, and 24% of the weighted ball group sustained an injury during training or during the season following the 6-week training. The injuries were stress fractures in the elbow and ulnar collateral ligament injuries. Two of the injured players in the weighted ball group showed the largest gain in external rotation of around 10 degrees.

From a purely anatomical and kinetic chain linking perspective, as you learned earlier, forced gain into external rotation will create tension on the inside of the elbow.

While I don't know specifics of the study, I do wonder if the injured players had a reduced total arc of motion to start, or if their motion was normal and forced into excessive ranges.

A link to Mike's description of this study[76] on his site can be found at www.UnleashPitchingVelocity.com/bonuses

Who is Weighted Ball Training Safe For?

In my opinion, given this latest clinical research, weighted ball training programs should be used in skeletally mature players (those who are well into, if not completely through, puberty), who have been examined for all the foundational throwing deficits, who have reached a velocity plateau using other training means, and have had their throwing mechanics checked by someone reputable and were found to be "clean." If I am describing you, you are likely safer than most to begin a training program like this.

Let's Review:

Weighted ball training is effective at increasing throwing velocity, but there is also a significant risk of throwing injury (in the high school pitcher) which both seem to be related to a gain in external rotation at the shoulder. Weighted ball training does not appear to increase arm speed and may not allow strength gains to be had on the throwing shoulder when combined with strength and conditioning programming.

Up Next:

In the next chapter are some of the more popular tools for gaining velocity and pitch command that are on the market today. I will go through the pros and cons of each, giving you insight for after you've completed your BASE-3 examination, to see which tool would benefit you the most.

For free bonus items, including a warm up/cool down routine, pocket guides, video demos, book updates, and more, visit: www.UnleashPitchingVelocity.com/bonuses.

Chapter 11
OTHER TRAINING TOOLS

There are countless numbers of drills and tools out there today. Each person has their own take on how to perform said drill, aimed at enhancing your pitching performance. I am sure all of these drills and tools were made with the greatest intent to help you become a better pitcher, and I'm positive they all work . . . on the right person, at the right time.

Some pitchers experience better results than others. One pitcher may increase velocity and improve command with one tool, while a different pitcher may find no lasting result with the same exact tool. Another pitcher may develop pain during drilling.

Why is that?

The Difference is in the Details

A simple answer could be that we are all different. Our bodies just work differently. It has different needs, and it responds differently to the same stressors.

I may see the same complaint from 10 different baseball pitchers, but their degree of problem and the root cause of their problem are not all the same.

For example, five pitchers walked into my office over a period of one month. Each pitcher had a primary complaint of dead arm with reduced velocity. I put each one through the BASE-3 System, and the results revealed their root causes were not the same:

- Pitcher A had a lack of spinal rotation to his throwing arm side.
- Pitchers B and C had weak external rotation strength.
- Pitcher D had poor dynamic control with a single leg squat, and very weak glutes.
- Pitcher E was one year out of shoulder surgery and had overhead and chest tightness, and thus lost the ability to fully lay back and reach his elbow behind his body.

Keep in mind that all of these problems listed above are common problems that occur in the baseball pitcher. A majority of these happen due to throwing itself: the side effects of pitching.

Let's take each of these pitchers who have the same complaint of poor velocity, but differing root causes, through some of the most popular pitching tools.

The Towel and Rope Drills

The drill consists of dry throwing with a towel in your hand or with ropes attached to a baseball. The bulk of the towel and rope is draped behind the forearm, and in a throwing motion, the intent is to pull the towel/rope through your delivery motion to get the towel/rope to snap at your release point. The goal of doing this drill is to get into a better, more repeatable delivery position with power, so you can throw harder.

Silent Side Effects and Drawbacks of the Towel or Rope Drill

Pulling the towel/rope through your delivery adds resistance to your acceleration phase of throwing. This will stress muscles like the Latissimus Dorsi, Teres Major, the Subscapularis, the Pecs, and the front core muscles. It will add strength to these muscles and could cause a bump in velocity. If the arm is moving faster, the posterior rotator cuff/deceleration muscles will have to contract harder, and this may increase decelerator strength, too.

But this may likely come at a cost. All those muscles I just mentioned will get tighter. If the pitcher, parent, or coach has no idea this is happening, this is setting up the pitcher for failure.

Additionally, the tools themselves are limited. You can only hook so many ropes on the ball, and you can only hold so many towels. Compare this to something like weight training where the load can always be increased.

Who are the Towel and Rope Drills Best Suited For?

If this were Pitcher A, adding more anterior core strength into his already lost motion into rotation is going to make him even tighter and won't fix his problem. He may see an initial bump in velocity due to strength gain, but I would expect this gain to be small and plateau quickly.

The *focus* of this drill is on pulling the arm through the delivery, so Pitchers B and C will not be strengthening their much needed posterior rotator cuff/back of the shoulder muscles. I would not expect these pitchers to see lasting success (but some success due to posterior cuff strengthening) with this drill. Furthermore, as the larger acceleration muscles are getting stronger and tighter, the deceleration muscles are becoming weaker.

Geek Out With Me! **Reciprocal Inhibition.** When muscles on one side of a joint are tight and over-activated, the muscles on the opposite side of the joint become inhibited. This is a process known as reciprocal inhibition. In its simplest form, when you contract the Bicep, the Triceps are inhibited so the elbow can bend. If you strengthened the Bicep to the point where they became tight (had resting tightness), this will actually "shut-off" or reduce nerve activation to the Triceps . . . rendering the Triceps just about useless.

Pitcher D could see some improvement with this drill from shear strength improvement, but it's unlikely to last, as his primary problem of leg strength and stability is not being addressed.

This drill would not help Pitcher E because it will not help improve tissue flexibility overhead or of the Pec. It will actually make this pitcher more tight.

Youth pitchers who have yet to develop tightness, and any pitcher whose coach is telling them they need to get out in front more, will benefit from this drill. I always defer to a pitching coach to tell me what me a pitcher's mechanical limitations are.

But if the mechanical limitations are preceded by biomechanical limitations, the only way to find that out is by going through the BASE-3 System, and getting on a plan to fix it. Only then will you get the most out of a rope or towel tool. If you want to learn more about the rope or towel drills, visit www.UnleashPitchingVelocity.com/ropedrill or www.UnleashPitchingVelocity.com/toweldrill

Olympic Style Weight Lifting

Olympic weight lifting is being used by the baseball pitcher to create power and explosiveness in their delivery. When performed correctly, it does this first by practicing the lifting movement pattern with minimal weight. Since most of these movements use the hips in an explosive way, it trains the hip muscles to contract explosively. It also helps many, many other muscles get stronger in the process. Weight is then added to the lift to help generate more strength.

Brent Pourciau of 3X Pitching was one of the first coaches, if not the first, to train pitchers in this manner. He has seen a lot of success with this method, but as you might have guessed, some pitchers do better than others.

Silent Side Effects and Drawbacks of Olympic Weight Lifting Proper Form

Most of the side effects of Olympic weight lifting come from training with improper form. If you begin this, or any kind of weight lifting, you should definitely work with a qualified coach to ensure you have proper form.

Just like pitching mechanics, sometimes you cannot get into the proper weight lifting positions because you don't have the necessary flexibility, strength, or control. If you begin an Olympic weight training program without knowing where your deficits are, you risk getting hurt or not being able to get the most of it.

Knees and Hips

One of the most common poor movement patterns I see during all forms of weight training are when the knees come closer together during squatting and jumping movements, like the image below.

Image 11.1:   Knees collapsing medially during a squat

Despite the lifting goals to increase explosive hip strength, this poor movement pattern further exacerbates hip weakness and will further ingrain poor pitching movements when driving from the rubber. Hip extension strength (Hamstring and Gluteus Maximus) will be improved (however, not to the maximum), but hip abduction strength (Glute Medius) will be limited. Overall, your gains and performance will be limited if this movement pattern persists. This can either be a neuromuscular deficit (mind-to-muscle connection) or a raw strength deficit of the hip abductors.

Low Back

Another concern is when the low back comes out of its straight back posture and rounds, like the image below.

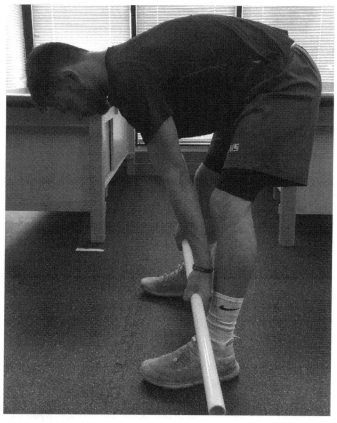

Image 11.2: Rounded low back during a dead lift

This posture will put more stress on the lower back, in addition to other areas. It will lead low back problems that arise from muscles or the discs of the spine leading to pinched nerves down the leg, also known as sciatica. Hamstring tightness, hip tightness, and core weakness will limit the body's ability to keep the back straight.

Elbow

The final concern with Olympic weight lifting is the supposed strain on the medial or inner elbow when catching a "clean," such as a hang-clean lift. While there are no studies that I could find that measured inner elbow strain, we can assume that there is some with certain lifts. How does this strain compare to pitching a baseball? We don't know. I do not think you should avoid Olympic weight lifting for this concern. If you're still skeptical, just avoid the catch on those lifts and perform a high-pull.

Acceleration vs. Deceleration

Olympic lifting places a heavy focus on explosiveness and acceleration. The deceleration muscles will get stronger, but don't forget about what you learned earlier regarding actual sport specific training down to the muscle action type. Olympic lifting alone will not train that for you, so you will need to add more programming to achieve your full potential and have maximum injury protection.

Who is Olympic Weight Lifting Best Suited For?

Pitchers A-E will all likely see gains if they have never performed this type of training before. However, since they are not getting to the main root cause of their issues, their performance will plateau and may even begin to regress. Additionally, placing performance on top of faulty foundation (fixing the top of the tower and not the bottom) is a quick way to start creating pain and reduced performance.

Pitcher D (leg weakness and poor control) has the most to gain from a program like this (if trained correctly) because it is directly targeting the root cause of their dead arm.

How could Pitcher A-E (excluding D) get the most out of a program like this? FIRST, LEARN AND FIX their foundational flaws, THEN begin the Olympic program, or do them concurrently.

Any pitcher can perform this kind of explosive movement pattern training, at any age. As a prerequisite, they must be able to understand the directions for proper form and have the ability to physically get into proper form. Legs begin the pitching motion, and they must be able to move quickly to enhance performance. Thus, Olympic weight training is an ideal tool if you are taking care of your other weak areas found in the BASE-3 System. If you want to learn more about Olympic pitcher training, please visit www.UnleashPitchingVelocity.com/Olympic

King of the Hill Trainer

Leg drive is an important factor in creating a high velocity pitcher. The King of the Hill trainer, created by Ground Force Sports, is a device that you stand on and pitch from. It gives the pitcher instant feedback if they are using their legs or not. Resistance can be increased to a point to help strength train the lower-half.

Side Effects and Drawbacks of the King of the Hill Trainer

The focus of this trainer is on rear leg drive. It will surely help to get more of that, but what if the stride leg is the problem leg? Putting more horsepower into a weak frame is not a good idea and will cause even more problems.

Take Jordan's example from earlier. Giving his rear leg more strength would not have helped his problem. He may have seen a bump in velocity due to the raw strength gain, but the root of his problem, his stride leg weakness, would not be getting any help. He may even have worse pitch command and begin to develop arm pain. Throwing gas on a fire is usually a bad idea.

Like most tools, this trainer is limited in that resistance cannot be increased beyond a certain point. If you're a pitcher who already has good leg drive and hear the feedback/click every time, how can you use this tool to get even better/more leg drive?

Who is the King of the Hill Trainer Best Suited For?

If Pitchers A-E are not using their legs/lower-half appropriately, this device will help them, but it will be limited due to their root causes not being corrected. Pitcher D will have the most to gain, again, because it's directly addressing his root problem. Any pitcher deemed by their coach as not using their legs may benefit from this tool. My advice, run yourself through the BASE-3 System, get on the program to fix your weak areas, and then begin using the King of the Hill trainer. If you want to learn more about the King of the Hill Trainer, visit: www.UnleashPitchingVelocity.com/KingOfTheHill

Core Velocity Belt

A creation by Lantz Wheeler of Baseball Think Tank, the Core Velocity Belt helps the pitcher to use the lower half effectively by creating powerful hip rotation, greater acceleration, and faster pitches.

A thick bungee cord is attached to the pitcher on the front or side of the drive hip. That cord is then attached to a spot on the floor in the path of the pitch delivery. When the pitcher goes through his delivery, the tension of the cord rotates his pelvis toward the plate, creating greater hip and shoulder separation. To me, this is different from most leg trainers out there, because the focus is on the pelvis and core.

Side Effects and Drawbacks of the Core Velocity Belt

The Core Velocity Belt "artificially" adds force in the beginning and middle of the kinetic chain by forcibly pulling/rotating you forward. Just like the leg drive training tools, putting more force into a dysfunctional system will create problems down the road. An initial bump in velocity may be seen using the Core Velocity Belt due to the shear speed of rotation increase and ground reaction force of the lead leg being produced. However, the remainder of the body may not be able to take on this added force for too long.

Who is the Core Velocity Belt Best Suited For?

Pitcher A, who has lost trunk rotation to the throwing arm side, may benefit from using this tool. The core velocity belt *may* forcibly rotate his/her pelvis and create greater rotation/hip and shoulder separation. This would allow more range of motion and thus more potential energy to be stored before the trunk accelerates forward, faster.

Of course, this may not happen at all. If Pitcher A has muscle, tendon, or joints that are reluctant to stretch with this tool, but instead needs a focused, low load stretching program, this tool won't help.

On the flip side of the coin, for Pitchers A-E, if it does increase rotation, there will be more force going through muscles, tendons, and joints that aren't used to it, starting at the stride leg and further up the chain all the way to the wrist. More force over time may lead to structural breakdown if the body doesn't adapt or it's not allowed to adapt due to too much throwing/not enough rest and recovery.

The Core Velocity Belt focuses on creating faster pelvic/trunk rotation and greater separation. After going through the BASE-3 System, and you are on a program to fix your weak areas, the Core Velocity Belt will be very beneficial for you if your goal is to throw harder. If you want to learn more about the Core Velocity Belt, visit: www.UnleashPitchingVelocity.com/CoreVelocity

VeloCon Trainer

An "armless" trainer, VeloCon (velocity + control), originally called The Arm Saver, was created by Frank DeMichele to help sync all parts of the kinetic train while not putting stress on the throwing arm. Instead, it uses a handle, rope, and tennis ball to give feedback about where the arm path should be. If you are moving your lower half and core correctly, the tennis ball slaps you at a predictable spot on your glove side elbow.

I think this device is tremendous, especially for the throwing arm injured or recovering pitcher, because it takes the arm completely out of the equation yet is still able to train proper movement of the legs and core.

Side Effects and Drawbacks of the VeloCon Trainer

The VeloCon Trainer's focus is making sure the kinetic chain is linked perfectly, all while not using the throwing arm. There is no added stress via weights or cords or bands. Once the kinetic chain is moving correctly, there is no way to enhance this tool for added force production. The VeloCon does not work with submarine type throws.

If the skill of using the VeloCon can be mastered in a few sessions, a pitcher can probably be pulled back into their improper movement patterns just as quickly. Constant monitoring is likely needed, but that shouldn't take much time.

Furthermore, if the trainer can be used correctly with a pitcher who has problems like the above, it goes to show that this tool is only a treatment tool, not a full-fledged examination tool; it cannot pick up on orthopedic problems that may actually be inhibiting throwing mechanics, velocity, and pitch command.

This tool also probably stays within the "averages" of pitching mechanics. Take Pitcher A, who has lost spinal rotation to the throwing side. If Pitcher A can master this tool within a few hours, his flexibility had to improve OR he is only staying within a certain range of trunk rotation to be successful with the drill. The latter is probably most true.

Who is the VeloCon Trainer Best Suited For?

The VeloCon is a great tool for practicing throwing with good technique when your arm is incapable of throwing, such as when rehabbing from an injury. You may have tried many other tools and pulled your body out of sync—The VeloCon Trainer may be a good tool to keep your kinetic chain movement in check.

For some pitchers that I have described earlier in the book, like taller pitchers, who from a BASE-3 standpoint are moving perfectly, but still have pain—this would be a good tool to check and see how their mechanics are functioning, then cross referencing this movement with actual throwing.

If Pitchers A-E all had mechanical dysfunctions identified by their pitching coach, the VeloCon trainer will help get their body back on track. However, this tool will never fix a weak rotator cuff, lost spinal rotation, increase hip strength and won't improve shoulder mobility. If you want to learn more about the VeloCon trainer, go to www.UnleashPitchingVelocity.com/VeloCon

Let's Review:

There are lots of tool on the market today, all vying for your attention and promising the same outcomes of throwing harder, with greater command so you can make the team of your dreams! Heck, that's this books' subtitle! While no one tool will work for everyone, certain pitchers may benefit more from one than others. Others might send you down the wrong road altogether and create injury. The trick is KNOWING what tool will work for you. The best pitching coaches want and need to know this information before having you use any tool. That's why I wrote this book, giving you and your coaches my BASE-3 System so you can truly maximize your results with any tool, program, or person you connect with. The subtitle of this book is my truth, because I believe I can help you, when you choose to focus on the right things.

If you want to learn more about any of these tools (more will be added to the bonus area over time), please go to www.UnleashPitchingVelocity.com/bonuses and check out their description links.

Up Next:

I want to teach you my exact examination process that I successfully use to reduce throwing injuries, bring players back from injury faster than ever, ensure the greatest pitch command, and unleash maximum velocity in the baseball pitcher. It is my hope that you will learn this process and be able to use it again, and again to not only be more proactive about preventing injury, but lay the proper foundation for velocity and performance enhancement. After you go through the BASE-3 System, *and corrected your "weak" links,* I can almost guarantee that you will be throwing harder, without pain, with greater control, and striking more hitters out. You will also have much more success working with pitching specialists to refine your throwing mechanics and process.

Section 4
The BASE-3 System

Chapter 12
STEP 1:
ASSESS FLEXIBILITY

The following chapters are going to rock your world. They're going to enlighten you about your body and show you the initial step you need to take to fix any problem or "weak" areas.

BASE-3 stands for:

Biomechanical
Athletic
Strength
Examination
3- The three steps of the examination: flexibility, strength, and control

I want to address the words "biomechanical" and "strength." Bio stands for biology, or body. Mechanical is how something moves. So biomechanical means how the body moves. Athletic further specifies the movements to be done.

Regarding strength, I am not only referring to strength in its well-known singular definition of muscle strength, but also how I would define *athletic* strength: strength of flexibility, strength of muscles, and strength of stability and control. When the components of the BASE-3 System are running on all cylinders, you are going to performing at your maximum. The physical will undoubtedly have an effect on the athlete's mental and emotional states, but that is beyond the scope of this book.

Players who have dominated the BASE-3 system—the ones who have near "perfect" scores—and not much corrective exercise programming are the players who make it to the next level. Your goal is to be like those players. Your exam results will give you the areas you need to correct. You correct them with a program tailor made for you, then you re-assess with the BASE-3 System.

Ideally, you run through the BASE-3 System every off-season and after every season of play. But you can do this every month to see what has been pulled out-of-whack and get it back on track.

Let's get started!

The first, and arguably most important, step in the BASE-3 System, is to find out where you are tight. There are 14 areas that you need examine, some on the upper body, and some on the lower body. I'm going to walk you through each of them here. I will break them up into 2 sections: Upper Body and Lower Body.

What You Will Need

Get My Video

Some items are a bit too detail oriented to include in this text and would be better understood if you could see it and hear me explain it. I highly suggest learning my tips for proper hand position, how much pressure to use for blocking structures (like the scapula), and how I grade certain hard to read tests by checking out my video walk-thru guide of the BASE-3 examination. You can find it at www.Base3Examination.com.

Download Your Worksheet

You'll also find a worksheet that you can use to mark your exam findings at www. UnleashPitchingVelocity.com/bonuses. I encourage you to download it and record your results, as it will give you a birds-eye view what areas on your body need the most work. It will also help to develop and see the first progression in your exercise program.

Find a Partner

For much of the examination, you will need a partner to help assess each test result. This can be a fellow ball player, parent, coach, or a friend you trust. If you would like to see the result for yourself, your partner can take pictures, or you can even use an application on your mobile device, like Apple's Facetime or a like service, so you can see in real time what your partner is seeing. On tests that a partner is needed, you will see "(Partner Mandatory)," and "(Partner Preferred)" when it's suggested, next to the test name.

Get a Goniometer

Last, we will be using a simple measuring device called a goniometer. Goni means "angle," meter is to "measure." This is how you will measure specific angles on the body. This is not a hard skill to learn, but can be confusing when you're just starting out. In light of this, I've created a short goniometer how-to video for you at www. UnleashPitchingVelocity.com/bonuses

Assess Upper Body Flexibility

I. Scoliosis Test (partner mandatory)

Rationale:

We are specifically looking at your ability to bend over to find out if you have any scoliosis. As mentioned earlier, scoliosis can have an impact on the height of your scapula and how the scapula moves.

Instructions:
1. Standing up nice and tall, bend over and attempt to touch your toes while not bending your knees. You may feel a nice stretch in your hamstrings.
2. Examiner: Stand behind the pitcher and watch them bend over.
3. Examiner: When they are at the bottom of their motion, look at the middle and top of their back, scanning from behind and over top of them.

If one shoulder or portion of the pitcher's upper back is significantly higher (toward the ceiling), this might indicate a rib-hump and tell us where a scoliosis curve is. Mark the outcome as Normal, Rib Hump Throwing Arm, or Rib Hump non-Throwing Arm.

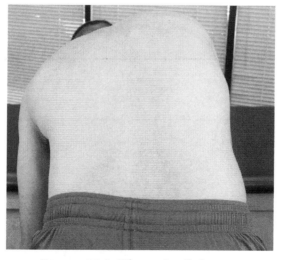

Image 12.1 Thoracic rib hump

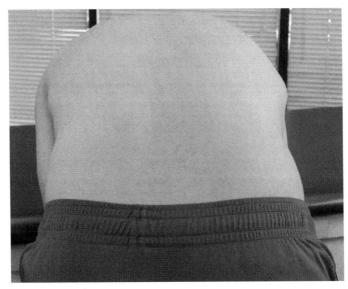

Image 12.2:   Normal thoracic spine bend without scoliosis

If you have a young athlete, especially one who hasn't hit puberty, and your test result reveals a rib hump that is new/undiagnosed, you should see your pediatrician or primary care provider ASAP. This test result may indicate a scoliosis curve that needs medical management to stop i's progression. In addition, this test is just to make us aware of any spinal curve which could affect the way the scapula moves.

2. Thoracic Rotation Flexibility (partner preferred)

Rationale:
Having a decreased ability to rotate your spine toward your throwing arm increases stress on the throwing shoulder and the inside of the throwing elbow. Hip and shoulder separation will not be optimal, and this will inhibit maximal throwing velocity and reduce control of the throwing arm as other kinetic chain links begin to compensate.

As a hitter, loss of hip and shoulder separation will reduce your ability get more speed and power on your swing.

Instructions:
1.   Stand up nice and tall.
2.   Keeping your feet pointed straight ahead and your hips pointed straight ahead, rotate your upper body toward the right.

a. Examiner can stand behind the pitcher and stabilize the pelvis/prevent it from moving to make it easier to assess maximal rotation.

b. Pitcher: If you are assessing this yourself, notice how far your shoulders move relative to the front of your body. Do NOT rely on how far you can see behind you because your head will turn and you will get a false result.

3. Rotate back to neutral and stop.

4. Now rotate to the opposite side, and compare.

a. Pitcher: Compare to the opposite side. Also, feel how this end position feels in comparison to the opposite side.

Pass-Fail Criteria:

Pay particular attention to how far the back shoulder rotates toward you, on each side. Assess the difference between each rotation, and record the result on your exam form: Normal, Tight Throwing Side, Tight Non-Throwing Side. We are looking for at minimum 45 degrees of hip and shoulder separation/rotation, to either side. But I really want you to focus on equality. The throwing side rotation should be at least equal, if not greater than, the non-throwing side. Use a PVC pipe, and look from above to help you, if needed.

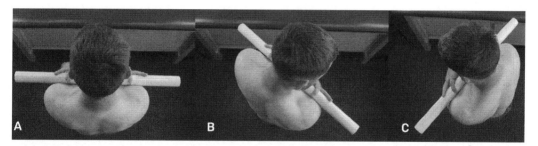

Image 12.3: A. starting position. B. full right rotation C. full left rotation.

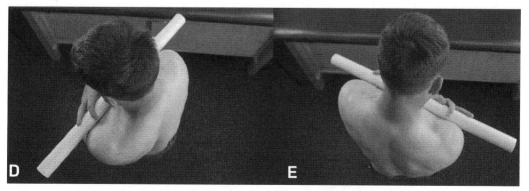

Image 12.4: D. test end on left, normal. E. test end on R, tight

If you are tight, perform the Thoracic Rotation Stretch Progression #1. Head to www.CommandThePlate.com/exercises to see how.

3. Overhead Tightness (partner mandatory)

Rationale:
As mentioned earlier in the book, your Latissimus Dorsi muscle is a strong internal rotator. If the "Lat" is tight on your throwing arm, this is going to limit external rotation or lay back and place more stress at your elbow. This will also alter the normal motion that occurs at your shoulder, placing more stress on structures like the labrum. A reduction in lay back is also correlated with poor throwing velocity. Like everything else, the tighter this muscle becomes, the less repeatability an arm path you can maintain.

Instructions:
1. Lie down on your back on an elevated surface such as a massage table or the end of your bed if you have a firm mattress. (This will work on the floor, but will be harder on your partner).
2. Have your partner lift your throwing arm up above your head as shown in the picture below.
3. At the same time, your partner, the examiner, should block your scapula from rising up by gently pressing on the lateral edge of the scapula bone as they can feel it pop up. Their pressure should not be super firm, but firm enough to keep it from moving, so they can assess how far your arm moves overhead without scapular compensation.

Pass-Fail Criteria:
With the scapula blocked, if the upper arm/bicep CANNOT line up with the ear, your overhead mobility (Lat or Teres Major) is tight. Repeat this on your non-throwing arm to pick up subtle differences in tightness. The arms should be equal and full.

The Tricep muscle could also be tight but is a bit too detailed to include in this text. I cover this and other more detailed tips and tricks in the video walk-thru of the BASE-3 System, which can be found it at www.Base3Examination.com

Mark your sheet for TIGHT or NORMAL for each side.

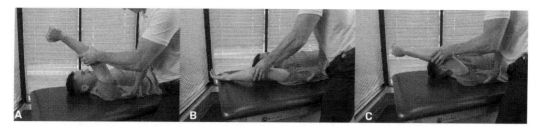

Image 12.5: **A.** test start. **B.** test end, normal. **C.** test end, tight

If you are tight, perform the Overhead Stretch Progression #1. Head to www. CommandThePlate.com/exercises to see how.

4. Pectoralis Major Tightness (partner preferred)

Rationale:
The "Pec Major" helps with assisting internal rotation and cross body motion at the shoulder. It has a moderately high muscle force output during the pitch and over time, can become tight and limit shoulder external rotation/lay back. As I'm mentioned earlier, loss of lay back is associated with lower throwing velocities and shoulder and elbow injuries. This is also a muscle that can get tight with poor posture.

Instructions:
1. Lie on your back on a firm elevated surface, such as a massage table. (This will work on the floor, but will be harder on your partner if you have one for this.)
2. Clasp your fingers behind your head and relax your arms.

Pass-Fail Criteria:
If any of your elbows CANNOT touch the table, you have tightness of your Pectoralis Major on that side, and this needs to be corrected.

Mark your sheet as TIGHT or NORMAL for each side. The throwing arm side is most important to address, if limited time is a factor.

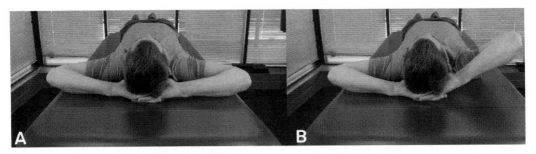

Image 12.6:   **A.** normal **B.** tight

If you are tight, perform the Pec Major Stretch Progression #1. Head to www.
CommandThePlate.com/exercises to see how.

5. Pectoralis Minor Tightness (partner mandatory)

Rationale:
The "Pec Minor" helps to stabilize the scapula when your cannon of an arm is
bringing the heat. Since the Pec Minor attaches to the front of the scapula, when it
gets tight, it tilts the shoulder blade toward the front, creating scapular dyskinesis,
and can inhibit the Lower Trapezius muscle from contracting strongly. This reduces
space in the shoulder socket, causing impingement problems, and can be a source
of pain.

Instructions:
1. Lie your back on a firm elevated surface, such as a massage table. This can
   work on the floor, but will be harder to assess for your partner.
2. Bring your arms down to the side of your body, as shown below, and relax.
3. Have the examiner find the two edges or tips of your Acromion process, the
   end most bony projection of the shoulder; it feels like a large square box on
   the top of the shoulder.
4. Grab the front of it and grab the back of it on each shoulder and see where
   they lie in relation to each other.
5. Notice the gap between the back of the shoulder and the table.

Pass-Fail Criteria:
If ANY shoulder is raised upward from the table, showing a large gap between the
table and the backside of the shoulder, this indicates Pec Minor tightness. You will
usually see the throwing shoulder Acromion process raised upward from the table

more than the non-throwing arm. This would indicate throwing shoulder Pec Minor tightness.

If both shoulders look the same, the examiner can press on the front of the shoulders to push them downward to touch the table. If the Pec Minor is not tight, there will be little to no movement of the arms. But if the Pec Minor is tight, when you press on the front of the shoulders, the arm will flail outward away from the body. Be sure to have the pitcher relax their arms before doing this. Explain to them, "I'm going to press on you, if your arms move, just let it happen."

Mark your sheet for TIGHT or NORMAL for each side.

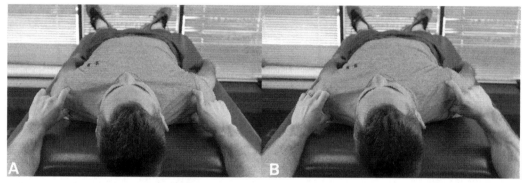

Image 12.7:   A. normal **B.** tight, notice the right shoulder elevated from the table with a larger gap under it compared with the opposite side.

If you are tight, perform the Pec Minor Stretch Progression #1. Head to www.CommandThePlate.com/exercises to see how.

6. Cross Body Tightness (partner mandatory)

Rationale:
Cross body tightness is an indicator of posterior shoulder flexibility. As you learned earlier, when the posterior shoulder/external rotators are tight, this limits internal rotation and the ability to properly decelerate across your body. This will place more strain on not only the shoulder structures but on the elbow.

Instructions:
1. Lie on your back on a firm surface.
2. On the throwing arm, have the examiner find the lateral edge of your scapula, which is a bony prominence that sticks out on the side of your body, as pictured below.

3. The examiner will grab this structure with the heel of their hand and block its motion. The pressure should be firm, but not cause the pitcher too much discomfort.

4. The examiner will then bring the arm across your body in line with your chin. As the examiner pushes the arm across the body, you will notice that the shoulder blade may want to follow. This is what he is blocking.

5. Take note of how far the elbow comes across the face on the throwing side, and compare this with the non-throwing side. Do not let the arm rotate overtop of the face.

Pass-Fail Criteria:

If the throwing arm side is NOT equivalent to the non-throwing side, this indicates tightness on the throwing shoulder and should be corrected. In general, I like to see the elbows come across, but below the face to in-line with the nose.

For hitters, if this motion is decreased on the lead arm of your swing, this will alter your swing mechanics, create greater demand from your spine and core muscles (placing them at greater risk of injury), which will ultimately limit your ability to hit for power.

Mark your sheet as TIGHT or NORMAL for each side.

Image 12.8: **A.** test start **B.** normal **C.** tight

If you are tight, perform the Cross Body Stretch Progression #1. Head to www. CommandThePlate.com/exercises to see how.

7. Forearm Supination Tightness (partner preferred)

Rationale:

The forearm pronators are part of the wrist flexor group of muscles in your lower arm. Pronation is the act of turning your palm downward to face the ground.

Supination is the opposite; turning your palm upward like holding a cup of soup. Did you hear it . . . soup as in supination?

The forearm forcefully pronates when you throw and your forearm "flexor-pronators" get tight and limit the opposite: forearm supination and wrist extension. A loss of supination can also correlate to a loss of the ability to stretch your elbow completely straight.

When your elbow cannot get completely straight, stress increases on your medial elbow, specifically the ulnar collateral ligament/Tommy John ligament.

Instructions:
1. Seated on a hard surface, with arms at the side of your body, bend your elbows to 90 degrees.
2. Starting with palms neutral and facing each other, rotate your palms upward, keeping your elbows at your side.
3. Compare one forearm or palm placement to the next.

Pass-Fail Criteria

If one palm cannot rotate completely upwards facing the ceiling, those pronator muscles on that side are likely tight and should be stretched.

Mark your sheet as TIGHT or NORMAL for each side.

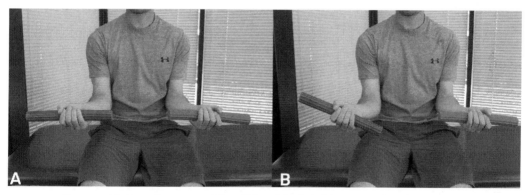

Image 12.9:   **A.** normal **B.** right sided tightness, note the subject holding a bar to make it easier to see

If you are tight, perform the Elbow Extension Stretch Progression #1 to improve supination. Head to www.CommandThePlate.com/exercises to see how.

8. Shoulder External Rotation (ER) Tightness
(partner mandatory)

This test and its counterpart, shoulder internal rotation tightness, is particularly difficult to follow along with text alone. So, I have recorded you a special video which can be found on the bonuses page at www.UnleashPitchingVelocity.com/bonuses. This is the quality of video you will see inside the BASE-3 walk-thru course.

Rationale:

I think we've probably beat this horse dead by now, but lost shoulder external rotation reduces layback when throwing. Lost lay back is correlated with lower throwing velocities, and greater amounts of medial elbow stress. External rotation is part of the total arc of motion at the shoulder. If there is a loss of motion somewhere in the total arc, this test will help us pinpoint its location.

There are a few different ways to measure the rotations at the shoulder. I use the following method, which has worked very well for the players I work with.

Instructions:
1. Lie flat on your back on a firm, elevated surface.
2. Abduct your non-throwing arm so it creates a right angle with your body, fist pointing upwards to the ceiling.
3. The examiner, your partner, places a rolled up hand towel under your upper arm, as shown below.
4. Actively lay back your arm into external rotation as far as it will go. Do NOT arch your back—this is important.
    a. If you feel a pinch on the back of your shoulder during testing, you need to place a 2nd towel under your arm to prop it higher.
5. Examiner takes this end measurement with a goniometer, and records the number on the exam sheet as ACTIVE Range of Motion for External Rotation.
    a. The stationary arm of the goniometer is pointed straight downward, perpendicular with the floor.
    b. The "zero" or start position of the goniometer is with the forearm pointed straight upward.
    c. The moving arm of the goniometer divides the forearm in half, pointing toward the center of the wrist on the lateral side of the forearm.

6. Examiner then pulls the arm into more external rotation, and continues to until the pitcher tells him/her to stop.
7. The pitcher tells the examiner to stop when:
   a. they believe they are at the end of their motion
   b. your back begins to arch, or
   c. if there is any pain at the shoulder or elbow.
8. Examiner takes a measurement with a goniometer and records on the exam sheet as PASSIVE Range of Motion for External Rotation.
9. Repeat on the opposite side, compare the difference.

To take some stress away from the inner elbow while doing this test, the examiner can flex the elbow to smaller than 90 degrees before they begin their passive range of motion testing.

There is usually greater amounts of external rotation on the throwing shoulder due to some front shoulder laxity or bony humeral retroversion that may have occurred. Regardless, this is not a problem unless there is a difference (less motion) in the total arc of external rotation and internal rotation combined.

This test represents half of the total arc of motion measurement. Internal rotation (IR) makes up the other half. Record both active and passive measurement numbers for ER.

Pass-Fail Criteria:
After you have measured internal rotation and found your TOTAL ARC of motion, you can specifically assess pass-fail for external rotation. The total arc of motion is ER measurement plus IR measurement (ER+IR = total arc) for both active and passive range of motion.

If your total arc of motion (active or passive) on the throwing arm is found to be less by greater than five degrees, you will then look to the individual ER and IR measurements to see what needs to be corrected. If throwing shoulder ER was tighter than non-throwing shoulder ER, then throwing shoulder ER tightness is a problem and needs to be corrected.

After you have measured IR to find your total arc, you can mark your exam sheet as TIGHT or NORMAL for the *throwing side.*

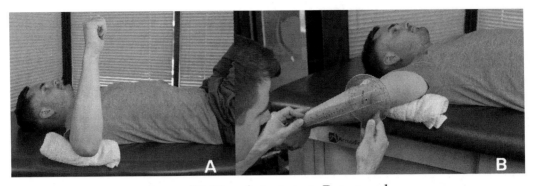

Image 12.10:   A. test start. **B.** test end

If you are tight into throwing shoulder ER, I recommend performing the Lat Stretch and Pec Major stretches to improve this. Strict ER stretches are not performed, unless supervised, as they can place strain on the inner elbow.

I don't usually see a loss of ER too often, but when I do, I also move to check the tightness of the Teres Major muscle and the Subscapularis muscle. Both of these tests are well beyond the scope of this book and can be somewhat tedious in their explanation. If you have ER tightness, I recommend that you make an appointment with a local sports physical therapist to get checked. You can find a board certified specialist, like me, near you at www.abpts.org by clicking "find a specialist."

It may be tough to find a therapist who specializes in treating baseball players, so I have included these extra examination details inside the BASE-3 examination video walk-thru found at www.Base3Examination.com.

9. Shoulder Internal Rotation (IR) Tightness
(partner mandatory)

Rationale:
The loss of shoulder internal rotation creates many problems at the shoulder, and elbow of the throwing arm, in addition to lost velocity.

Again, if you're an audio-visual learner, head to www.UnleashPitchingVelocity. com/bonuses and let me teach you this technique via video.

Instructions:
1. Lie flat on your back on a firm, elevated surface.
2. Abduct your non-throwing arm so it creates a right angle with your body, fist pointing upward to the ceiling.

3. The examiner, your partner, places a rolled up hand towel under your upper arm, as shown below.

4. Keeping your upper arm in the right angle position, actively rotate your arm down toward the floor, into internal rotation. Be extra careful NOT to *slide* your arm inward closer to your body and coming out of the right angle you started in.

    a. Before you start this motion, the examiner will moderately push down on the front of your shoulder to block any scapular motion that wants to occur.

5. The examiner takes this end measurement with a goniometer and records the number on the exam sheet as ACTIVE Range of Motion for Internal Rotation.

    a. The stationary arm of the goniometer is pointed straight downward, perpendicular with the floor.

    b. The "zero" or start position of the goniometer is with the forearm pointed straight upward.

    c. The moving arm of the goniometer divides the forearm in half, pointing toward the center of the wrist on the lateral side of the forearm.

6. The examiner then pushes the arm into more internal rotation, still with pressure on the front of the shoulder, and continues to until the pitcher tells him/her to stop or if the arm simply cannot move anymore.

7. The pitcher tells the examiner to stop when:

    a. they believe they are at the end of their motion

    b. there is any pain at the shoulder or elbow.

8. Examiner takes a measurement with a goniometer and records on the exam sheet as PASSIVE Range of Motion for Internal Rotation.

9. Repeat on the opposite side, compare the difference.

10. Add the numbers for ACTIVE motion for throwing shoulder ER and IR together. This is your total arc of motion for active range of motion.

11. Add the numbers for PASSIVE motion for non-throwing shoulder ER and IR together. This is your total arc of motion for passive range of motion.

Since there are usually greater amounts of external rotation on the throwing shoulder, there are usually less amounts of internal rotation. The total arc of motion is just shifted toward the backside, but should be equal, greater, or within five degrees of the non-throwing shoulder.

Pass-Fail Criteria:

After you have measured internal rotation and found your TOTAL ARC of motion, you can now assess Pass-Fail for either external or internal rotation.

If your total arc of motion (active or passive) on the throwing arm was found to be *less* by five degrees or more, you have failed this test. You will then need to look at the individual ER and IR measurements to see where the problem is. If throwing shoulder IR is tighter than the non-throwing shoulder IR, then throwing shoulder IR tightness is a problem and needs to be corrected.

This test result will generally correlate with tightness on the Cross Body test. If one is tight, usually so is the other.

Mark your exam sheet as TIGHT or NORMAL *for the throwing side.*

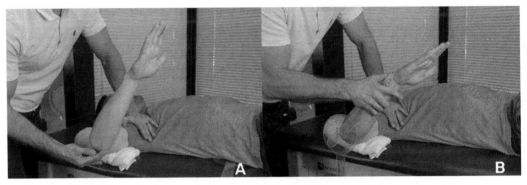

Image 12.11:   **A.** test start **B.** test end

If IR is the problem motion, perform the Modified Sleeper Stretch. Head to www.CommandThePlate.com/exercises to see how.

Assess Lower Body Flexibility

I. Ankle Mobility

Rationale:

We are specifically looking at the length of the Soleus muscle, the calf muscle that resides under the larger and more recognizable Gastrocnemius muscle on the back of your leg. A loss of motion here can make it harder to squat, thus affecting the depth and control of your squat, limiting power production, which will directly affect your ability to use the "lower half."

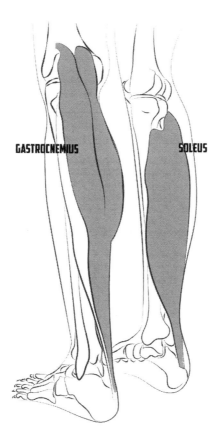

Figure 12.1: Soleus & "Gastroc" muscles

Instructions:
1. Find a wall. Measure 9cm from the base of the wall and place a strip of athletic tape parallel with the wall at that 9cm mark, as shown below. The leading edge of the tape should be at 9cm (If you have a baseboard on the wall, approximate the width of the baseboard and subtract it from your 9cm distance . . . effectively moving the tape closer to the wall making up for the baseboard.)
2. With shoes and socks off, place your toes on the leading edge of the tape.
3. While keeping your heel on the ground, bend your knee forward to attempt touching the wall with your knee.

Pass-Fail Criteria
If you cannot touch your knee on the wall without lifting your heel, you have restrictions in the ankle and you must fix this.

Mark your outcome on your exam sheet as TIGHT or NORMAL, for each side.

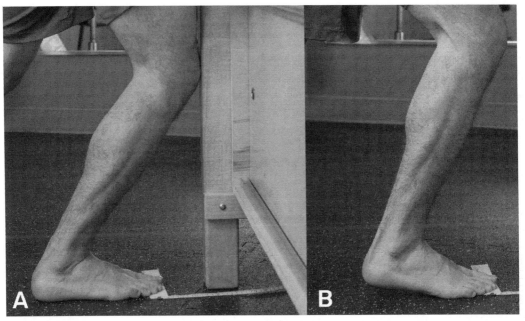

Image 12.12:   **A.** test end with a normal result. **B.** tight test result, notice how the heel is raised off the floor, and also the knee cannot touch. Either of these conditions represent a "tight" test.

If you are tight, perform the Soleus Stretch Progression #1. Head to www. CommandThePlate.com/exercises to see how.

2. Hip Flexor Tightness (partner mandatory)

Rationale:
If your trail leg hip flexor is tight, this could inhibit your stride length and cause early (or late) rotation of your thoracic spine. If the hip flexors are tight, this will naturally inhibit the hip extensors (the glutes) from contracting at their maximum. This will result in low throwing velocity and less repeatability of your pitches.

Instructions:
1.   Sit on the edge of a table or your bed if it has a firm mattress.
2.   Lie back and bring your knees upward so they make a 90-degree angle with your body (knees pointing up to the ceiling), as shown in the picture below.
3.   With your hands, hold the right knee in place. (Do NOT pull the knee closer to your chest or let it fall.)

4. Drop the left leg and see where it rests; Examiner scores.
   a. It's very important that the pitcher really relax here and let the left leg drop.
5. Repeat on the opposite side.

Pass-Fail Criteria:

If the thigh does not reach parallel with the floor, the pitcher has a tight hip flexor.

   If the knee does NOT passively bend (at rest) to approximately 90 degrees, the pitcher also has a tight Quadriceps.

   Mark your outcome on your sheet: TIGHT or NORMAL for each side.

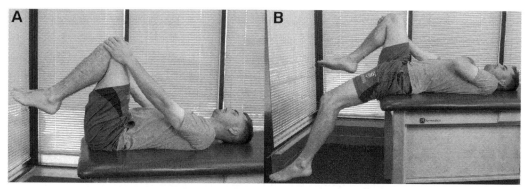

Image 12.13:   **A.** test start. **B.** test end, normal. When I passively bend the left knee, it can make a 90-degree angle with the thigh *without* the thigh moving.

Tight variations:

Image 12.14:   **C.** hip flexor tightness (thigh not parallel to floor) **D.** Quadriceps tightness (thigh parallel, but knee rests very straight) **E.** both hip flexor and Quadriceps tightness

   If you are tight, perform the Hip Flexor & Quadriceps Stretch Progression #1. Head to www.CommandThePlate.com/exercises to see how.

3. Hamstring Tightness (partner preferred)

Rationale:

I am primarily concerned with your stride leg hamstring flexibility. The hamstrings are a group of muscles that often inhibits the knee from becoming straight because of the high eccentric forces that go through it to decelerate the body.

The highest velocity pitchers that maintain longevity in their career do not sink into their delivery on the lead leg. Rather, they catapult off that leg as the knee becomes straight. If the hamstring is tight, it will cause you to sink into your delivery, or it will cause your upper-half to compensate, thereby reducing your velocity and further affecting your command or repeatability with every throw as this muscle continues to get tighter.

Instructions:
1. Lie down on your back on a firm surface.
2. Keep your right leg flat on the table/floor.
3. Have the examiner lift up the left leg as far as it will go, keeping the knee completely straight.
   a. Pitcher: Alternatively, you can use a strap to lift your own leg up if you don't have a partner.
4. The examiner should also stabilize your right leg from lifting up. I like to sort-of straddle the athlete using my knee on the athlete's thigh to block this leg.
5. Compare this with the opposite side.

Pass-Fail Criteria

If the stride leg CANNOT achieve a 90-degree angle with the body (get straight up), the hamstring is tight and should be corrected.

Mark your sheet as TIGHT or NORMAL for each side.

Image 12.15: **A.** test end, normal. **B.** test end, tight result, with strap.

If you are tight, perform the Hamstring Stretch Progression #1. Head to www. CommandThePlate.com/exercises to see how.

4. Thoracic and Lumbar Extension Range of Motion
(partner preferred)

Rationale:
In order for the spine to fully rotate, it must extend. Those two motions go together. A loss of thoracic or lumbar extension can place more stress on the front side of your shoulder by forcing it to externally rotate more. If the arm can adapt, great. If not, this is a problem. If you have more strain on the front of the shoulder, you can bet that, too, of the elbow. Eventually, this causes a breakdown. Pain is generated, and velocity is lost.

Instructions:
1. Lie face down on a firm surface.
2. Place your hands just above your shoulders.
3. Relaxing all the muscles on your back, including your Glutes, press your upper body up, extending your elbows using only your Triceps.

Pass-Fail Criteria
There should be evidence of a nice connected curve coming from between the shoulder blades down through the lower back. Additionally, the pelvis bones should be very close to resting on the table

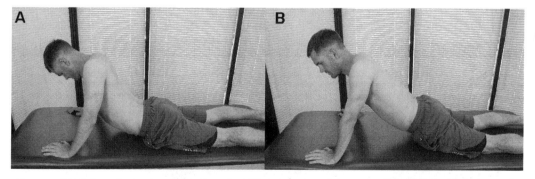

Image 12.16:   **A.** test end, normal with connected curve of the back. **B.** test end, tight with a straight back.

Evidence of a hinge (like a door hinge) means *excessive* motion is occurring at that single joint in the back.

If you see a hinge somewhere in the low back (evidenced by a skin fold [a line made by folding skin] across the back, OR a very steep curve like the image below [contrast this with Image 12.16A], there is a good chance there is a lack of range of motion above or below the hinge. If you see a hinge in the motion, improving motion here should only be done by a professional as you don't want to make the hinge any worse.

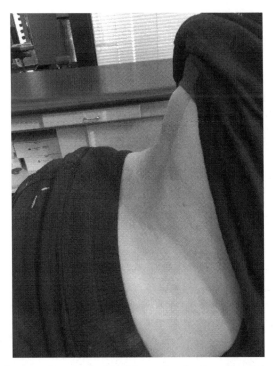

Image 12.17:   evidence of a probable hinge in the low back by a steep curve with motion occurring at one joint at the bottom (and none at the joints above).

If you see a rather straight spine or a pelvis that lifts completely off of the table, like the tight example above (12.16 B), WITHOUT evidence of a hinge, then you can be correct this with stretching and mobility work.

Mark your sheet as TIGHT or NORMAL.

If you are tight, perform the Spinal Extension Stretch Progression #1. Head to www.CommandThePlate.com/exercises to see how.

5. Hip Internal Rotation (partner preferred)

Rationale:

A loss of hip internal rotation will place more stress further up the kinetic chain. If the stride leg hip cannot internally rotate, it's like a 10-car pileup; the hip comes to a dead stop, and all parts of the kinetic chain that come afterward crash. In this case, the parts that come afterward compensate and take on more stress.

Instructions:
1. Lie on your stomach on a firm surface.
2. Have the examiner bend your knees to 90 degrees and gently push your feet outward away from each other, effectively internally rotating your thighs/hips.
3. Measure with a goniometer or eyeball the distance. If you are using a goniometer:
   a. The stationary arm of the goniometer is pointed straight upward to the ceiling, perpendicular with the floor.
   b. The "zero" or start position of the goniometer is with the shin bone pointed straight upward.
   c. The moving arm of the goniometer divides the shin bone in half, pointing toward the center of the ankle on the front side of the lower leg.
4. Compare each side to each other.

Pass-Fail Criteria:

If both legs look equal and are at least 35 degrees as measured with a goniometer or eyeballed, you are in the clear. If one hip is less internally rotated than the other, specifically on the stride leg, this must be corrected.

Mark your sheet as TIGHT or NORMAL for each side. If the drive leg is tight, this is optional for you to correct, as the stride leg is most important.

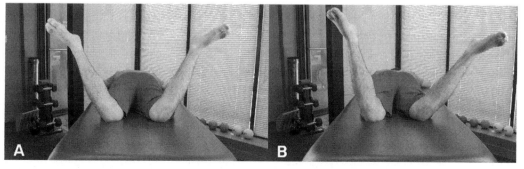

Image 12.18:   A. test end, normal. **B.** test end, left leg tight.

If you are tight, perform the Hip Internal Rotation Stretch Progression #1. Head to www.CommandThePlate.com/exercises to see how.

6. Glute Tightness (partner preferred)

Rationale:
Tightness on your glutes is particularly problematic on the stride leg. If your glutes are tight, this can also limit the amount of internal rotation on your stride hip, causing mechanical dysfunction, lost velocity, and increased stress up the chain.

Instructions:
1. Lie on your back on a firm surface.
2. Have your partner, the examiner, passively flex your right hip to 90 degrees.
3. While keeping this hip flexed to 90 degrees, your partner will externally rotate your leg, attempting to bring your foot above your opposite hip bone.
4. Your partner should stop when you tell them it cannot be stretched any more—you are at your limit.
   a. Alternatively, you can attempt to pull your leg yourself, and compare sides with vision and feel.
5. Take a measurement with the goniometer or eyeball the measurement. If using a goniometer:
   a. The stationary arm of the goniometer is pointed downward toward the foot OR upward to the head.
   b. The "zero" or start position of the goniometer is with the shin bone pointed straight.
   c. The moving arm of the goniometer divides the shin bone in half, pointing toward the center of the ankle on the front side of the leg.
6. Repeat on the opposite leg. Compare differences.

Pass-Fail Criteria
Ideally, I would like to see around 70 degrees of hip external rotation measured on each leg, as shown below. If you have less than this, you have a tight glute and this should be corrected.

Mark your sheet as TIGHT or NORMAL for each side. The stride leg hip is most important. If your drive leg is tight, correct this if you have time.

Image 12.19:   **A.** test start, right leg. **B.** test end, normal right leg
C. test end, tight left leg.

If you are tight, perform the Glute Stretch Progression #1. Head to www.CommandThePlate.com/exercises to see how.

7. Groin Tightness (no partner needed)

Rationale:
If your groin/hip adductor muscles are tight, this will limit the distance you can spread your legs apart. Tight groin muscles will create early spinal rotation and will directly have an impact on the ability to create good hip and shoulder separation. This will lead to a loss of velocity and compensations up the chain which can lead to injury. This is also important as a hitter.

Instructions:
1. Lie on your back on a firm surface, legs straight.
2. Take your right leg, cross it onto your left leg, resting the outside of your heel just below your knee cap.
3. Ensure the pelvis is flat/not rotated off the floor. Notice my hand stabilizing the pelvis in the image below.
4. Look at the height of your shin bone (from your angle as the pitcher, it will be the calf); it should be almost parallel with the floor.
5. Repeat on the opposite side.

Pass-Fail Criteria:
The shin bone should be almost parallel with the floor. If it is not, or in order to get the shin parallel, the pelvis rocks, the groin muscles are tight and need to be corrected.

Mark your exam sheet as TIGHT or NORMAL for both sides. Both legs are important to focus on.

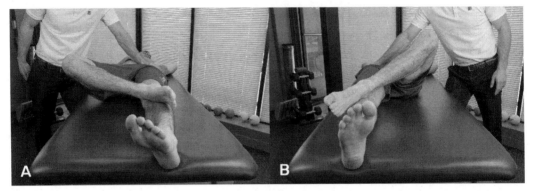

Image 12.20:   **A.** test end, normal on right leg. **B.** test end, tight on left leg.

If you are tight, perform the Groin Stretch Progression #1. Head to www. CommandThePlate.com/exercises to see how. Both sides are equally important to address.

Up Next:

Step 2 of the BASE-3 System. How to assess muscle strength.

Chapter 13
STEP 2:
ASSESS STRENGTH

Assessing strength with manual muscle testing is a skill that is learned and honed over the course of one's early career as a medical professional. With that being said, I do not expect you to be super accurate and spot on with any type of meticulous grading system. I will simply ask you to test either side and measure as strong or weak.

What You Will Need

How to Test

A good measure for how strong someone should be at any particular muscle is to be able to hold resistance against *almost* maximum effort. I stress the word "almost" because the last thing I want you to do is use all of your might to press down on the athlete's extremity and cause an injury.

With that being said, the risk of injury in muscle testing is very low. A general rule of thumb is to initiate gentle pressure and then consistently, over 5 seconds, add more and more until you feel you're around 75% of your (the tester's) maximum pressure.

A muscle that is weak is going to fatigue enough in those 5 seconds for you to give it the grade of "weak." If a muscle is not fatiguing, or the joint is not "breaking" (moving), then as long as you're confident in your pressure grading, you can give the grade of "strong."

Find a Partner

You will need a partner for all muscle testing. You will either have to teach your partner how to test or give them this book.

Watch the Video

Again, if you are interested in learning my tips for proper hand placement, supportive holds, how I grade certain hard to read test results, and many more tips and suggestions, I strongly suggest checking out my BASE-3 System walk-thru guide. Find it at www.Base3Examination.com.

Upper Body Strength Testing

I. Shoulder Scaption

Rationale:
The Deltoid muscles are the prime movers of the shoulder, helped by the stabilization strength of the rotator cuff. If this is weak, you can almost bet that all the other shoulder muscles will also be weak.

This is the one strength test that near maximal pressure does not need to be achieved. You can press down with approximately 50% effort and hold there and see which arm begins to fatigue. Since you're pressing with less force, hold for longer time of 10 seconds.

Instructions:
1. Pitcher sits on a firm surface.
2. Have the pitcher raise their arms up in the shape of a "V" in front of their body, parallel with the ground, with their thumbs pointed upward toward the ceiling, as shown below.
3. Standing in front of the pitcher, the examiner will place their hands on the top side of the pitcher's forearm just above the wrist.
4. Press down over 10 seconds grading up to 50% of your maximum pressure.
5. The pitcher tries to resist your pressure/their arm from falling.

Pass-Fail Criteria:
If either arm, or both, fatigue at the same time before 10 seconds, they're considered weak and should be strengthened.

Mark your exam sheet as STRONG or WEAK *for the throwing arm.* The non-throwing arm is important, but not mission critical to your velocity, control, or arm health.

Image 13.1:   Testing position for shoulder scaption.

If you are weak, perform Scaption Strength Progression #1 head to www. CommandThePlate.com/exercises to see how.

2. External Rotation at the Side

Rationale:

If the external rotators are weak, the evidence is stacked against you to have a throwing injury compared to someone who is not weak. You can also expect your rotator cuff will not be able to decelerate your arm, and your velocity will suffer as a result.

Instructions:

1. Sit on a firm surface, arms at your side, elbows flexed to 90 degrees, palms facing each other.
2. Rotate the arms slightly outward approximately 5 degrees.
3. Standing in front of the pitcher, the examiner will place their hands on the outside of each of the pitcher's forearms just above the wrist, as shown below.
4. Grading up to 75% pressure over 5 seconds, the examiner will try to press each of your arms in toward your body at the same time, as you resist.

5. The examiner will compare one side's strength to the opposite side, and mark the exam sheet. One-sided weakness will be easy to feel and see by testing both arms at the same time.

6. In addition, the examiner will repeat this test one arm at a time, standing to the side of the pitcher. When repeating one arm at a time, the examiner will also visualize and use their opposite hand to feel the scapula.

Both arm testing Pass-Fail Criteria:

If either arm, or both, fatigue at the same time before five seconds, they're considered weak and should be strengthened.

Mark your exam sheet as STRONG or WEAK *for the throwing side.*

One-arm testing Pass-Fail Criteria:

If the scapula pops off of the back, or if you can feel the medial edge of the shoulder blade more when you are applying resistance to the arm, this indicates scapular instability. In addition to the rotator cuff being weak, if it tests that way, the scapular stabilizers also need to be strengthened.

Mark your exam sheet as NORMAL or SCAPULAR INSTABILITY *for the throwing side.*

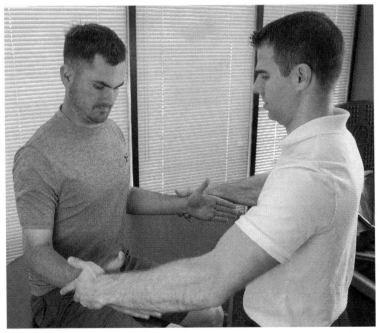

Image 13.2:   Testing position, both arms for ER at side

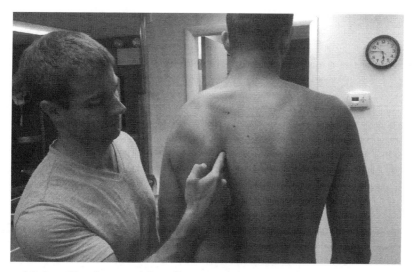

Image 13.3:   Testing position for one arm ER, with (+)positive scapular instability. Note how you can see the whole medial edge of the scapula bone just above my finger.

If you are weak, perform External Rotation Progression #1. Head to www. CommandThePlate.com/exercises to see how. Scapular Instability Progression #1 is included in the same exercise. As a hitter, your non-dominant side is also important to strength train. But as I mentioned earlier in this book, your dominant arm is likely going to be weaker, and your focus should be here as a pitcher.

3. Internal Rotation at the Side

Rationale:
Internal Rotation will not usually test weak. The muscles that create internal rotation are much larger and inherently stronger than the muscles on the opposite side of the shoulder. If internal rotation does test weak, it's usually in the pitcher who hasn't yet hit puberty.

Instructions:
1. Sit on a firm surface, arms at your side, elbows flexed to 90 degrees, palms facing each other.
2. Rotate the arms slightly inward approximately 5 degrees.
3. Standing in front of the pitcher, the examiner will place their hands on the *inside* of each of the pitcher's forearms just above the wrist, as shown below.

4. Grading up to 75% pressure over 5 seconds, the examiner will try to press each of your arms outwards away from each other at the same time, as you resist (this is the exact opposite test of external rotation).

Pass-Fail Criteria:

If either arm, or both, fatigue at the same time before 5 seconds, they're considered weak and should be strengthened.

Mark your exam sheet as STRONG or WEAK *for the throwing side.*

There is not usually one-sided weakness with this test, so it's not important to test one arm at a time. You do not need to look at the scapula when testing internal rotation strength as the scapula does not play a vital role when internally rotating the arm at the side.

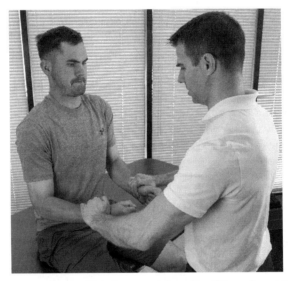

Image 13.4:   Testing position for IR at the side.

If you are weak, perform Internal Rotation Strength Progression #1. Head to www.CommandThePlate.com/exercises to see how.

4. External Rotation at 90 Degrees

Instructions:

1. Sitting on a firm surface, abduct and externally rotate your throwing arm into a high-cocked position (a "90-90" position), with knuckles pointing to the ceiling.

2. Rotate your arm into slight internal rotation, like the image shown below. Knuckles are pointing more forward.

3. The examiner will stand to the side or slightly behind the pitcher and place their hand on the *back* of the pitcher's forearm just above the wrist. The opposite hand can gently prevent the upper arm from falling during testing.

4. Grading up to 75% pressure over 5 seconds, the examiner will try to press your arm downward into internal rotation as you resist.

5. Repeat on the opposite side.

Pass-Fail Criteria:

If the arm fatigues before 5 seconds, it's considered weak and should be strengthened.

Mark your exam sheet as STRONG or WEAK *for the throwing side.*

Image 13.5:   Testing position for ER at 90 degrees.

If you are weak, perform 90-90 ER Strength Progression #1. Head to www.CommandThePlate.com/exercises to see how.

5. Triceps

Rationale:

The Triceps muscle group are a very important muscle to rapidly extend your elbow and continue velocity and acceleration on the ball. If it's weak, your velocity will suffer.

Instructions:

1. Lie down on your back on a firm surface.
2. Flex your shoulder to 90 degrees with respect to your body and bend your elbow to 45 degrees (or 135 degrees) as shown in the image below.
3. The examiner stands over top and to the side of the pitcher and applies pressure to the lower end of the forearm just above the wrist.
4. Grading up to 75% pressure over 5 seconds, the examiner will try to press your forearm downward into a more bent elbow as you resist.
5. Repeat test on the opposite side.

Pass-Fail Criteria:

If the arm fatigues before five seconds, it's considered weak and should be strengthened.

Mark your exam sheet as STRONG or WEAK *for the throwing side.*

Image 13.6:   Testing position for Triceps strength.

If you are weak, perform Triceps Strength Progression #1. Head to www. CommandThePlate.com/exercises to see how. The non-dominant arm is unimportant for throwing, but important for hitting.

Also, I rarely find weakness when testing the Biceps, except in young athletes who have yet to enter puberty. If you would like to see how I test Biceps strength and learn more tips not included here, check out the video walk-thru of the BASE-3 System at www.Base3Examination.com.

Continue on to learn how to assess lower body strength.

Lower Body Strength Testing

1. Hip Abduction

Rationale:

Weakness of the hip abductors will affect the control of your squat. It will also affect the amount of force transfer from your lower half to your upper half and from one leg to the next leg. Weakness on your stride leg hip will result in inconsistent throws due to inconsistent placement and pelvis instability. Abduction weakness on the drive leg will affect the ability to power your "lower half" toward home plate . . . making it very difficult to use your lower half. Weakness will also keep you to a shorter stride length.

Instructions:
1. Lie down on your side on a firm surface.
2. Kick your top leg up and slightly backwards to either 11 o'clock if you're lying on your right side, or 1 o'clock if you're lying on your left side. Your leg should only be lifted away from your opposite leg around 25 to 30 degrees, as shown in the picture below.
3. The examiner stands behind the athlete, placing his/her hand on the lower leg just above the ankle on the outside of the leg. The opposite hand can rest on the Glute being tested to feel the muscle contract.
4. Grading up to 75% pressure over 5 seconds, the examiner will try to press your leg down toward the leg on table. The pitcher resists. Mark your exam sheet.
5. Repeat on the opposite site.

Pass-Fail Criteria:

If the leg fatigues before five seconds, it's considered weak and should be strengthened.

Mark your exam sheet as STRONG or WEAK for each side.

Hint: these muscles are often very weak in baseball pitchers. If these muscles seem drastically weak compared to all the other tests, you are testing accurately!

Image 13.7:   **A.** Testing position for hip abduction strength. **B.** Same testing position from a bottom view to show leg backwards to 11 o'clock while lying on the right side.

If you are weak, perform Hip Abduction Strength Progression #1. Head to www.CommandThePlate.com/exercises to see how.

2. Hip Adduction

Rationale:

I am most concerned with your stride leg hip adductor muscles. If this muscle group is not strong, it will have a hard time pulling your pelvis, and thus your core and torso toward the front in order to continue acceleration for your upper half. The hip adductor supports the deep core muscles, such as the Obliques and the Transversus Abdominis, to rotate your body toward the front, powerfully closing the hip and shoulder separation you once had.

Instructions:
1.   In the same side-lying position as testing abduction, bring your top leg and cross it over your bottom leg so your foot rests in front of your opposite leg. If you can get your foot flat, even better!
2.   Raise up your bottom leg as high as you can.
3.   The examiner, standing behind the athlete, places their hand on the inside of the lower leg just above the ankle.
4.   Grading up to 75% pressure over 5 seconds, the examiner will try to press your leg down toward the table. The pitcher resists.
5.   Repeat on the opposite side.

Pass-Fail Criteria:

If the leg fatigues before five seconds, it's considered weak and should be strengthened.

   Mark your exam sheet as STRONG or WEAK *for the stride leg.*

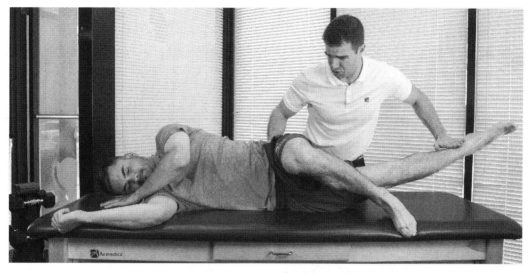

Image 13.8:   Testing position for hip adduction strength

   If you are weak, perform Hip Adduction Strength Progression #1. Head to www. CommandThePlate.com/exercises to see how.

3. Hip Extension

Rationale:

Hip extension is important on both your drive leg and your stride leg. Again, if your hip muscles are weak, you will have a hard time being able to use your legs in your pitching delivery. You'll have a hard time lengthening your stride and carrying force through that stride, which will limit your velocity. You will also won't be able to decelerate forces when you need to.

Instructions:
   1. Lie on a firm surface, face down.
   2. Lift one leg up until your thigh is off the table, as pictured below.
      a. Ideally, you're lifting up just high enough so your toes are equal with your heel of your opposite leg. Make sure you're not kicking up so high where your spine and pelvis begin to rotate or your back begins to arch.

3. The examiner stands above and to the side of the pitcher, places his/her hand directly over the back of the knee. The opposite hand can rest on the Glute you are testing.

4. Grading up to 75% pressure over 5 seconds, the examiner will try to press your leg down toward the table. The pitcher resists.

5. Repeat on the opposite side.

Pass-Fail Criteria:

If the leg fatigues before five seconds, it's considered weak and should be strengthened.

Mark your exam sheet as STRONG or WEAK for each leg.

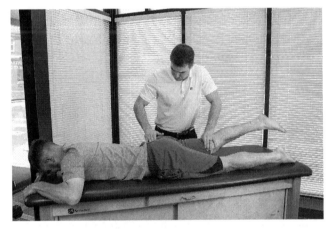

Image 13.9:   Testing position for hip extension strength

If you are weak, perform Hip Extension Strength Progression #1. Head to www. CommandThePlate.com/exercises to see how.

4. Hamstrings

Rationale:

The hamstrings are a very important muscle group on your drive leg to help extend your hip (in conjunction with the Glutes) and generate power. They're also very important muscles on your stride leg that help decelerate the body near the end of a throw. If your hamstrings are weak, you won't be able to generate maximum force from your drive leg, nor will you be able to decelerate maximum forces near the end of your throw, which could lead to injury.

Instructions:
1. Lie on your stomach on a firm and elevated surface, if able.
2. Bend one knee to 90 degrees.
3. The examiner stands at the foot of your table near your feet and places one hand on the back of your bent lower leg just above your ankle. The opposite hand can rest on the hamstring you are testing.
4. Grading up to 75% pressure over 5 seconds, the examiner will try to pull your leg straight, down toward the table. The pitcher resists. Mark your exam sheet.

Pass-Fail Criteria:
If the leg fatigues before five seconds, it's considered weak and should be strengthened. Mark your exam sheet as STRONG or WEAK for each leg.

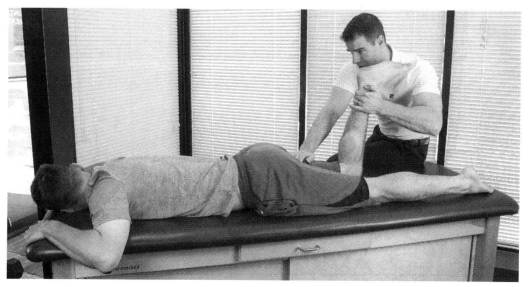

Image 13.10:   Testing position for Hamstring strength

If you are weak, perform Hamstring Strength Progression #1. Head to www. CommandThePlate.com/exercises to see how.

5. Anterior Core

Rationale:
More than adequate tension needs to be developed across the front side of the pitcher's body. All the force the legs have created will not be built upon by the

anterior core if it cannot develop tension. The upper half will become disconnected as speed and momentum are lost. Velocity will obviously suffer, and more strain will be placed on links further up the chain; scapula, shoulder, elbow, etc.

Instructions:
1. Prop yourself into a plank position, like the picture shown below. Use an examiner to help check your form:
2. Do not sag your lower back, but do not prop your butt too high; be like a *plank* of wood—straight.
3. Your elbows should be shoulder-width, but rest in front of your shoulders.
4. The forearms stay parallel with each other.
5. You should be up on your toes (you'll test best with shoes on).
6. You should be trying to push your upper body through or between your shoulder blades so you have a flat or rounded upper back (you don't want to see the shoulder blades popping off your back).

Pass-Fail Criteria:
The GOAL is to hold this position for two minutes. Any deviations, such as:
   a. sagging in the lower back
   b. buttocks popping upward
   c. prominence of the medial edges of the shoulder blades
   d. rotation of the forearms away from parallel

. . .indicate a breakdown and the timer should be stopped.
Mark your exam sheet as STRONG or WEAK and record your time.

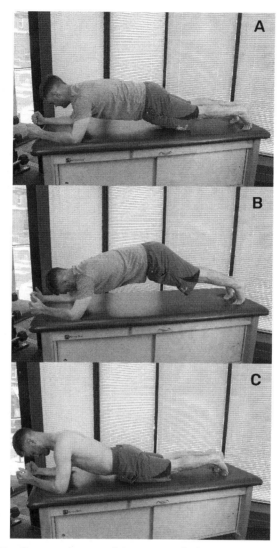

Image 13.11: **A.** Perfect testing position **B.** Failure with butt high **C.** Failure with saggy back, forearms are not parallel, and scapula's visible off the back

If you are weak, perform the Anterior Core Strength Progression #1. Head to www.CommandThePlate.com/exercises to see how.

Chapter 14
STEP 3:
ASSESS DYNAMIC CONTROL

What good is having great strength, power, and flexibility if you are unable to control it? Think about the tall child going through puberty. Think about rounding a curve in your car just after you gave it too much gas. Think about most people's golf game—all have the power but are lacking control.

It does not matter how much strength and flexibility you have if you cannot put it toward movement to complete a task with excellence. In this case, your task is throwing a baseball. The following are two basic movements, which if not performed correctly, negatively affect your pitch velocity and command.

Single Leg Squat

Single Leg Squat Rationale

The ability to move well on one leg is critical to the baseball pitcher. The pitcher drives off one leg and lands on the other. If one of those legs are deficient in strength, power, or flexibility, that effects balance, which affects control.

Balance and Control

On the surface, you might think balance and control are the same, but they are not. Balance is the ability to maintain upright without falling over. Control is more performance based. Control is the ability to adapt to changing situations without a loss in performance or output. Essentially, it's the ability to control your balance at any given time, while maintaining or creating strength and power to complete your task. It's the downhill skier whose one ski gets away from them, but acts like it never happened and actually gains speed down the mountain. It's the baseball pitcher who, despite fatigue late in the game, can still keep hitting spots and earning K's, and may actually begin to throw harder.

The Lower-Half Kinetic Chain

The primary rationale for looking at your single-leg squat form is to see how the kinetic chain is moving in the lower half, on each the stride leg and the drive leg, irrespective of muscle strength. I've seen pitchers with excellent strength have very poor dynamic control and stability. On the contrary, I've seen excellent control from pitchers who are very weak.

Loss of stability from the drive leg will allow the knee to collapse inward or the pelvis to drop. Either will undoubtedly create a breakdown in pitching mechanics from the get-go, and your command will suffer. The knee collapse or pelvic drop will also allow strength/force to leak from the system. All that force you are trying to generate from the ground will not make it into your delivery, and your velocity will suffer.

By properly strengthening the hips and teaching the body to move correctly in more challenging sport specific positions, you will be able to throw harder than you ever thought possible and have greater command . . . Yes! just by "correcting" your hips.

Instructions:
1. Take off socks and shoes.
2. Stand on one leg.
3. As the examiner, ask the pitcher to squat on one-leg, up and down, five times.
   a. Squat down as low as you feel comfortable, then come right back up.

Feel free to video record this, and watch it in slow motion if to help you make the right assessment, below. I've been assessing this for years, so it comes very natural and easy to me.

Pass-Fail Criteria:
To PASS the test, we are looking for the pitcher to squat down, keeping his/her pelvis level and keeping the hip, knee, and foot in a straight line: no rotations, no collapses. I also want to see the pitcher's knee bend close to 90 degrees.

You FAIL the test if:
- The pelvis/belt-line drops away from parallel with the floor
- The upper leg/femur rotates inward. You will be able to see this by looking at the knee cap. If the knee cap points inward, the femur is also rotating inward.

- The knee dives or collapses inward.
- The knee angle does not bend near 90 degrees (shallow squat), also often accompanied by a forward bend of the trunk.

Mark your examination sheet as NORMAL or ABNORMAL for each leg.

Image 14.1: **A.** Normal form, front view. **B.** Knee dives/collapses inward, also with the upper/leg femur rotating inward. **C.** Pelvis tilts away from parallel

Image 14.2: **A.** Shallow squat with forward trunk bend
B. Normal form squat from side view

If you are ABNORMAL, perform Squat Progression #1. Head to www. CommandThePlate.com/exercises to see how.

Some Extras

The knee should only do two things: the knee should straighten, and the knee should bend. If you see any other deviation from straightening or bending, such as a rotation or a collapsing inward, it's either coming from the hip or a collapsing of the arch (pronation) on the foot. Sometimes it can be both.

I always prefer to start with strengthening and adding control to the hip to fix this. Arch strengthening is not very effective and the only other treatment option is orthotics. I would not use orthotics in kids who haven't hit puberty—their foot is changing too much. However, I have seen a nice slip-on arch support that has worked with a few of my patients for controlling motion. You can find it at www.UnleashPitchingVelocity.com/bonuses.

Upon further testing after strengthening, if the hips are very strong and the single-leg squat is still poor, despite practicing, AND you also see the foot pronating or the medial arch of the foot collapsing . . . only at this time will I try to correct the knee motion from the foot.

Rarely is single leg squat form poor if the hip has become very strong and there is no foot deviation.

Another deviation commonly seen in the single leg squat is a pelvic drop. When the pitcher is standing on one leg and squatting, we're specifically looking at the opposite hip. If the pitcher is squatting on their left leg, our eyes are on their right hip/pelvis, and we're watching to see if that right hip drops. Ideally, we want to see that pelvis stay completely level, and not like 14.1 C., above.

Tip!

If the pitcher reaches backward with his non-squatting leg, he will be more likely to show a pelvic drop. My advice is to NOT prompt the first few reps the pitcher squats, but rather watch how they do it. Then, do a second round of squats and prompt them. See if that makes a change. If it does, great, but you still need to make that change squatting with the leg back.

Tip 2!

If the pitcher aces the single leg squat test, repeat the same test but have them jump straight up and down on one leg. There is no need to make the jumps quickly repetitive. Jumping up and down will force more stress into the system, and make it easier to see problems if they are going to show.

If you are not used to watching and assessing quick movement (not many people are), it may help to record these jumps with your smartphone, etc., to watch in slower motion. Grade the test the same way as above.

Scapular Dyskinesis

A scapula is one of your shoulder blades. You have two shoulder blades or scapulae that sit on the top of your back.

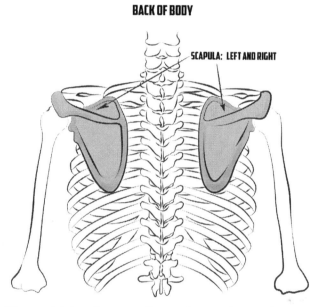

BACK OF BODY

SCAPULA: LEFT AND RIGHT

Figure 14.1: image of scapulae on bony skeleton

Scapular dyskinesis (dis-ky-knee-sis) simply means the abnormal movement of one or both shoulder blades compared to normal.

In addition to caring how the scapulae move, we also want to look at what resting position they start from. This can give us clues into how they might be moving and indicate other problems that are occurring.

Water Cannon

If the player has abnormally moving scapulae, they cannot throw as hard or as far as they are capable of. Picture a large war cannon sitting on the ground. You light the fuse, and the cannon ball flies out with a certain speed and lands some distance away. Now contrast that image with a cannon sitting inside a canoe, which is sitting in a lake. You light the fuse just like before, watching and comparing what happens. Which cannon ball goes farther? Which carries more speed?

I pose these same questions to all the players I examine who have scapular dyskinesis. Ninety-nine percent answer correctly; the remaining 1% aren't paying attention to me in the first place—kids these days!

Yes, the cannon ball fired from the canoe in water is not going to travel as fast or as far as the cannon firing from the ground. It will not, because it lacks a stable base or platform to fire from.

Cannon of an Arm

You may have been told that you have a cannon for an arm. You also throw a ball. Your scapula is the platform which your cannon (rotator cuff, Teres Major, etc.) sits on. If you have abnormal scapular positioning or abnormal scapular motion (dyskinesis), you will not be able to throw as far or as hard as you are actually capable of because you lack a stable base. You could also be at greater risk of injury.

Geek Out With Me! **Scapular Dyskinesis and Injury.** A study by Meyers[77] published in 2013 looked at 246 high school baseball players over 2 seasons. They analyzed injury risk for those that had verified pre-season scapular dyskinesis. Players who had scapular dyskinesis did experience throwing-related injuries, but not more so than players who had normal moving scapulae. The results of this study are in line with others that show not everyone who has scapula dyskinesis experiences shoulder pain, but frequently those with shoulder pain have scapular dyskinesis.

What Normal (and abnormal) Looks Like

In order to learn if you have scapular dyskinesis, let's begin with what is considered normal.

When looking at your pitcher from the front, you should see that both shoulders are the same height and the collarbones gently angle or point upward nearing the tip of the shoulder. What you will commonly see is that one shoulder sits lower. This is common in the baseball pitcher, but not normal, and needs to be corrected.

In about 90% of the population, the dominant shoulder sits lower. The shoulder often gets pulled even lower in throwing athletes. It's thought to be due to the high eccentric muscle forces that pass through the shoulder.

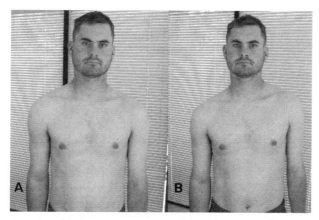

Image 14.3:   Front view **A.** Shoulders level **B.** Dominant shoulder sitting lower (most common to see, but not normal)

When looking at your pitcher from the side, you should see the head seated very slightly in front of the shoulders. The ear should line up just in front of the tip of the shoulder. What you will commonly see is the shoulders will be rounded toward the front and the head slightly protruded. Poor sitting posture, too much text messaging, and throwing can lead to chest tightness and a forward chin posture.

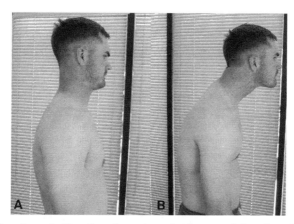

Image 14.4:   Side view **A.** Ear lined up just in front of the shoulder tip/acromion **B.** Shoulders rounded forward, head drastically protruded

When looking at the pitcher from the rear, again shoulder heights should be equal. When looking at the shoulder blades themselves, you might just barely be able to make out their most medial or inner edge. From that medial edge nearest the spine, touch the blade and find its lowest point and highest points. The line that makes up the medial edge attaching the two points should angle outward from top to bottom. The blades should look and feel pretty flush with the body.

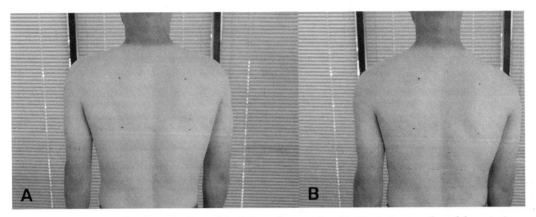

Image 14.5:   Back view **A.** Equal height of scapulas **B.** Dominant shoulder sitting lower, notice the dots on the upper and lower most points

Any deviation from this position is considered abnormal. Well, kind of . . . I'll explain later.

When we ask the pitcher to move both arms overhead in front of him/her, the scapulae should rotate upward (the medial edge rotates away from the spine) and stay flush against the body as the arms move to beside the ears. You will most likely always see this happen. In addition, you may even see the dominant arm shoulder blade rotate upward more than the non-throwing arm; that is usually normal.

Now, as you ask the pitcher to slowly lower their arms, the shoulder blades should *still* stay flush on the body. You should not be able to see any edge or corner of the blade that lurches off the body. If you do, this is abnormal.

I again repeat this test asking the player to move his arms out to the sides and overhead like a jumping-jack, and then slowly back down.

Types of Dyskinesis

The most common types of scapular dyskinesis I see are when:

1.   The bottom most point of the scapula is very visible (Type I)

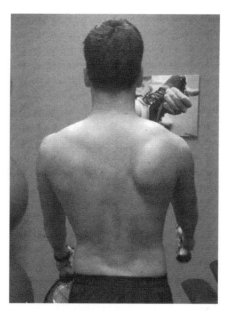

Image 14.6: Type I scapular dyskinesis on the right side in a mature athlete. This is problematic because it's not identical to the opposite side.

2. The whole medial edge is visible, sometimes including the top or highest most point of the scapula (Type II).

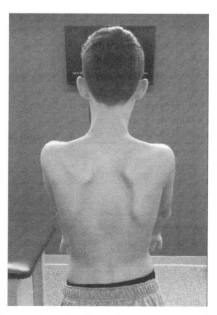

Image 14.7: Type II scapular dyskinesis, greater on the right side in a youth player. The right side is not identical to the left and represents a problem.

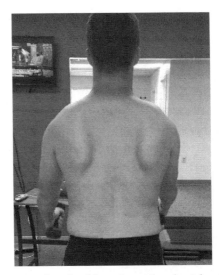

Image 14.8:   Type II scapular dyskinesis on both sides in a mature athlete. Since the athlete is mature, I would consider both sides problematic if they are complaining of pain or decreased performance.

Each type, if present, can mean different things. For our purposes, we will be just indicating if scapular dyskinesis is PRESENT or NORMAL.

Geek Out With Me! **Grading Scapular Dyskinesis**. Ben Kibler, MD came up with a scapular dyskinesis grading system[67]. He had recognized three types or grades of scapular dyskinesis, and one grade for normal. When research on this classification method was completed, the grading system was found to have poor reliability. This meant that it was rare that two or more skilled clinicians could agree on the same grade. I happen to like the grading system, which is why I'll expand on the two most common types that I see. Use the information as a fun fact, or help it drive your examination further. No matter the type, the program you are building for yourself, via your BASE-3 System results will include a plan to address any and all deviations.

Causes of Abnormal Positioning and Motion

Scoliosis

Most of us have heard the term scoliosis. It means an abnormal twist or curve of the spine. It can happen to different parts of the spine and in different severities.

Scoliosis is usually diagnosed before puberty and can be minimized with proper bracing, if needed at all.

Scapular positioning and movement is usually affected when the curve occurs in the Thoracic spine. Depending on what side the curve is on, it will place one shoulder blade higher and the opposite lower. The abnormal scapular position will obviously affect how it moves, but that doesn't mean it will be problematic. The scapula is still at risk of moving abnormally as described just above, in addition to its poor initial placement. Scoliosis may place the pitcher at greater risk of throwing injury and reduced performance, but the body can also adapt over time to compensate for this change. Sometimes adaptations are good; other times they are not.

Youth Age

Ninety-five percent of the time, I see abnormal scapular resting position and movement in youth players. The reason is simple: they are weak. In my experience, the muscles that control the scapula are usually not developed in younger athletes. Thus, I see both shoulder blades that look identically abnormal. If they are not identical, there is a problem.

If the muscles do not have the strength to hold the scapula in the resting position, they certainly do not have the strength to perform proper movement . . . especially when throwing a baseball. If the scapula isn't moving correctly, more stress is placed on everything else down the chain.

I often tell parents of youth players that I am not concerned about an identical scapular abnormality. As the pitcher physically matures, their scapular muscles will gain strength and the dyskinesis will resolve. But, I never want to leave this up to chance, especially with all the repetitive throwing this athlete may do. So, I always say, "Since we found it, we might as well fix it."

I believe the reason we don't see more youth athletes with arm injuries is because the majority cannot throw hard and excess stress isn't compounding down the chain. However, those who throw too often will eventually create problems from the sheer volume of throwing.

Youth athletes that can throw harder tend be a little heavier and more developed. I see less scapular problems in these players, but these athletes are often utilized more, such as throwing for many teams, and playing high volume throwing positions, such as pitcher and short-stop, or catcher.

These athletes resemble older pitchers where I see more one-sided scapular problems. If the shoulder blades do not look identical, surely there is a problem.

In this case, the scapula itself is not the problem, but is the result of some other breakdown that came before in the kinetic chain, such as:

Loss of Strength

The majority of youth players will have scapular dyskinesis from lack of strength, specifically of the scapular muscles. But, as I mentioned last chapter, if weakness is evident in the earlier parts of the kinetic chain, no matter the age, excess muscle force will be tossed up the chain. This excess force will overload the scapular muscles and cause them to weaken.

Loss of Flexibility

Strength may not be so much an issue at the scapula, but muscular tightness can be. On a more global view, if range of motion is diminished earlier in the kinetic chain, there is less ability of that link and subsequent links to dissipate force. Not only does this lead to muscular weakness, but all that overload of force causes specific muscles to get tight.

Specifically, if the external rotators are tight, this limits internal rotation and cross body motion. Since the shoulder and arm need to move into internal rotation and across the body to properly decelerate, it becomes a problem when it cannot. The scapula compensates by moving further laterally and forward around the body. The scapular muscles which attach on that medial edge get overstretched with every throw and can create pain right at the shoulder blade[78]. A more laterally displaced scapula can create Internal Impingement at the shoulder.

Poor Neuro-muscular Control

This is a pitcher who has poor control of the shoulder blade when you watch him/her move, but you can then get them to move properly with some specific instruction. Basically, this athlete has a poor ability to connect the dots from mind to muscle and just needs a little help to learn how to move correctly. Proper strengthening in combination with this instruction is the ideal treatment.

Instructions for assessing scapular control:
1. As the examiner, have the pitcher stand still, arms at the side, and look at them from the front, side, and back.

2. Record any and all of your findings in your own words (Right shoulder low, left collar bone is flat, complete medial boarder prominence, etc.) on the exam sheet. This will give us some clues for how we might expect the shoulder to move—this is just for your knowledge, and potential pieces of the puzzle.

3. Ask the pitcher to lift his/her arms out to the front and overhead, biceps by the ears and stay there.

4. Ask the athlete to slowly bring arms down, in exact reverse of how they got up there, and watch the scapulas closely. Ask them to repeat this 5x. Record your findings as PRESENT or NORMAL.

5. Ask the athlete to lift his/her arms out to the side and overhead, like a jumping-jack, and stay there.

6. Ask the athlete to slowly bring arms down, in exact reverse of how they got up there, and watch the scapulas closely. Ask them to repeat this 5x. Record your findings as PRESENT or NORMAL.

If you do not see any deviations, repeat steps 3 through 6 with 3-to-5 lbs. of weight. This will place more demand on the shoulder, and bring about deviations in the scapula, if there are any. There is nothing special about the exact weight. If you only have 2 lbs., use that, it's better than nothing . . . or find some heavier water bottles to lift. Ideally, you want to see smooth motion during testing. If the athlete struggles to lift the weight, it's too heavy and weight should be lessened.

If you need to video record this and watch in slow motion, go for it.

If scapular dyskinesis is PRESENT, perform Scapular Progression #1. Head to www.CommandThePlate.com/exercises to see how.

What Your Test Results Mean

Type I Dyskinesis (bottom most tip of blade is prominent).

Tightness:
The Pectoralis Minor muscle could be tight. The "Pec" Minor is attached to the frontward projection of the scapula, known as the coracoid process. If this muscle becomes tight (from poor posture, throwing without proper training for flexibility and strength), it pulls the coracoid forward and downward, effectively tipping the scapula forward, allowing the lower most tip to protrude off the back.

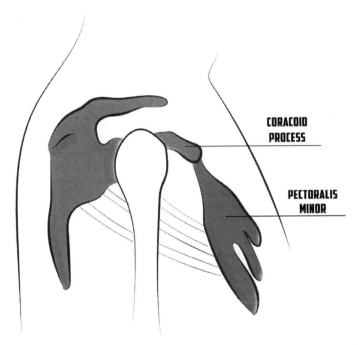

Figure 14.2:   Side view of a right shoulder showing the scapula with coracoid process and Pectoralis Minor attaching to the ribs. If the Pec Minor is tight, it tips the scapula forward impinging the structures below it (rotator cuff tendons, bicep tendon, bursa).

Weakness:

The Lower Trapezius and Serratus Anterior muscles could be weak if you see this deviation when the arms are returning from being lifted out to the front. When you see this deviation upon return from the jumping-jack position, it additionally means the Middle Trapezius is weak.

In the first part of your examination, if you found tightness of the Pec Minor and a scapula that has Type I movement, you can be sure that Pec Minor tightness is part of the problem. We should also assume the above mentioned scapular muscles are weak, and drop them in our program to be strengthened.

Type II Dyskinesis (whole medial edge of the blade is visible).

Tightness:

As briefly mentioned above, the posterior shoulder can be tight, weakening the scapular muscles and allowing the whole scapula to float laterally and the medial boarder to lurch off the back. Additionally, the Pec Minor can also be tight. Can you see why testing is so important?

Weakness:

I generally see Type 2 dyskinesis in youth athletes who have global weakness. I also see this type in people who have joint laxity/excessive flexibility, and generally in taller players.

This orientation of the scapula places the ball more to the front of the body, increasing the risk of shoulder subluxations and dislocations.

If you have found Type 2 dyskinesis, consider all of these scapular muscles weak: Serratus Anterior, Lower and Middle Trapezius, and the Rhomboids.

Post Examination Concerns

One piece of advice to keep in mind after you have gone through the BASE-3 System and got on *the correct plan* and successfully fixed your "weak" or problem areas: the pitcher may have greatly improved their strength, have no more tightness, and have excellent control while moving about during the exam. However, on the mound they seem to move exactly the same—why is this?

This is most likely because the pitcher has an ingrained movement pattern when throwing—they simply are stuck in the old way of moving, despite having the new bodily ability to move differently, and better.

To overcome this will take a great pitching coach to simplify the pitching process and get the pitcher to feel and get use to their new movement patterns. This can be a quick turnaround (i.e., one day), or can take weeks to improve just one area. It really does depend on the abilities of the coach and the athlete alike.

Let's Review:

Single leg control is very important to have for the baseball pitcher. If the knee collapses inward or the hip drops during a single leg squat test, this indicates poor control of the entire leg and will negatively affect mechanics, pitch repeatability, and velocity. This must be corrected with strength, flexibility, and balance training in various situations.

Scapular dyskinesis is the abnormal position or movement of the shoulder blades. Many things can cause this, such as muscle weaknesses, tightness, and specific bony alterations. Scapular dyskinesis is likely the result of tightness and weaknesses elsewhere on the body, especially if it is only seen on one side. Most youth pitchers have dyskinesis on both scapulae, and while it may not be a problem now, it should be addressed.

This was the third and the final part of the BASE-3 System. It's comprehensive, and I understand it may seem overwhelming. Take one step, one part at time. Break it down into as many sub-sections as you need, but most important, get it done. If you need help or want more detailed guidance, I encourage you to check out the video walk through of the BASE-3 System to expedite this process.

Up Next:

Now that you have the examination tools and the knowledge that I have, you have one thing left to do: put it into action! An examination does nothing more than tell us what we need to work on. Now that your exam is complete (or will be very soon!) I want to show you what to do with the results of each test. I am going to give you a quick tutorial on how to use www.CommandThePlate.com to rapidly increase your strength in your weak areas, quickly improve your flexibility in your tight areas, and develop the proper control so you can unleash your pitching velocity!

Chapter 15
COMMANDTHEPLATE.COM

The first question I always get when I tell a pitcher, their parents, or their agent that something is tight, weak, or has poor control is, "*How do I correct it?*" I don't want you to go halfway on this process to unleashing your pitching velocity and command and just stop. The examination is vital, but it is only HALF of the process. The real magic comes when you take the exam results and correct your "weak" areas. Because of this, I want to officially introduce you to Command the Plate baseball pitcher training program.

This chapter is not meant to be a full tutorial on CommandThePlate.com. After the exam, you have many results. To get you started, I have given you access to the first of many progressions that make up a well-rounded program to increase your strength, flexibility, and control in these key examination areas. The first step will get you started, but you **absolutely must continue beyond the basics** with a progressive plan to get you to the level you want to be. For example, after you complete basic progression #1 of hip abduction strengthening, you need to progress to the next most challenging exercises to train your hip even further: progression 2, 3, 4 and sometimes 5. The whole progression is included in Command the Plate training program, and you can sign up at www.CommandThePlate.com.

Step #1 is to enter your results from the examination sheet to the website. When you do this, the website will automatically tell you what exercise progression will best correct your weakness, tightness, or poor control and give you a link to view the exercise.

Step #2 is to click that link which takes you to a video page/ video explanation, by yours truly, of how to perform this exercise properly. What to avoid, what bad form is, etc. What happens next is awesome. . .

Image 15.1:   Screenshot of video page

Step #3. This exercise will be automatically put into an online flow sheet for you to track your progress daily/weekly, add your weights, band color resistance, etc. You will even be able to print this flow sheet out or just open it up on your mobile device and record on the go.

	Outcome	Progression 1	Progression 2	Progression 3	Progression 4
Static Observation					
Ankle Mobility	Tight	Soleus stretch	Gastroc stretche	Lax ball	Kel S. MWM
	Normal	--			
Scoliosis Test	Normal				
	Rib Hump on Throwing Arm				
	Rib Hump on non-Throwing Arm				
Dynamic Stability	Abnormal	BW Squat	SLS, weighted	SLS jumps	
	Normal	SLS, weighted			
Thoracic Rotation	Tight Throwing Side	supine T/S stretch			
	Tight non-Throwing Side	supine T/S stretch			
	Normal	--			
Scapular Dyskinesis	Present	TB Row c ER (1a)			
		Dynamic Hugs (1 Push up + (start	Scap planks (3b)		
		Prone HorABD (1c)			
	Normal	--			
Lumbar Extension RO!	Tight	Press ups	Foam Roll techniques		
	Normal	--			
Prone Plank Hold	Weak	Prone plank (tak	Torture Twists & Reverse Toture Twists		
	Strong	Torture Twists & Reverse Toture Twists			
Prone Quad Tightness	Tight	Supine RF c strap			

Image 15.2:   Screenshot of online exercise flow sheet

On the exercise video page itself, there is even a box for you to leave your own notes or questions for me, or to remind yourself to post in the group forum.

Step #4. Once you hit the goal achievement for that particular exercise, you click the "Goal Achieved" button near the top of the video page and are immediately taken to a new video page to begin the next progression. This exercise will also automatically replace the prior progression in your flow sheet.

Image 15.3:   Screenshot of Goal Achieved button

If you've ever paid a professional to examine you AND write a unique program for you or your pitcher, you've likely spent a few hundred dollars, or even many hundreds of dollars month-after-month for continued progressions.

The examination which you have just learned puts this knowledge into *your* hands. The automated guidance for *your unique* exercise progression is done for you. It literally takes the guess-work out of what to do next. You don't have to be a professional trainer or have any sort of physical education background. I structured it this way because I know if you follow the plan, you will see results and achieve your baseball goals.

In general, the Command the Plate training program is not meant be a complete strength and conditioning program; it's meant to *fit into* a strength and conditioning program. Ideally, I'd love you to zip through the BASE-3 examination, pass everything with flying colors (no tightness, no weakness, and no control problems), and get on to a full, proper strength and conditioning program.

I have these programs available, and your CommandThePlate.com trainings will seamlessly fit right into the programming.

For the youth pitcher, this program **will be** well rounded enough to be a complete program. A youth pitcher who does anything to better their body will help their game tremendously. Now you have access to the proper exercises to get the most out of your body.

For the more mature pitcher (high school and beyond), CommandThePlate.com is surely not a full strength and conditioning program, but is a program specifically designed to correct your foundational weaknesses, which most strength and conditioning programs don't take the time to do or don't focus on enough.

When you start your account at CommandThePlate.com, your program exercises can float right into a full strength and conditioning program that changes with your season (in season, off season, summer season, fall season) and changes based on the days rest you have (1-to-6 days' rest). The best part, it's unique to you! This isn't cookie cutter garbage.☺

If you haven't set up your account at www.ComandThePlate.com yet, do it now and get started on your path to Unleash Your Pitching Velocity!

Some of the steps #s and automation functionality listed above are still in development at the time of writing this book. It is my full intent to make sure they are working properly by the time you join www.CommandThePlate.com, but sometimes technology can create hiccups. Regardless, all of your exam results will still be tracked, and you will still know exactly what exercise progressions to focus on. You will never be lost in what to do. I can't wait to hear of your success! Join now: www.CommandThePlate.com

Chapter 16
CONCLUSION

Okay, right now you're probably feeling a bit overwhelmed and on information overload. That's okay! It would be amazing if all this information was immediately absorbed and 100% useable from the get-go. If you're like me, I highlight, underline, make notes, and dog-ear pages that stood out so I can go back and really soak up the information.

Use this book as your guide from season-to-season, year after year. You now have the power, knowledge, and tools to constantly re-examine, re-evaluate, and make changes to your program based on your unique examination results. If your pitching performance all of sudden starts to decline, re-examine. If you have an ache or pain on your body, re-examine. Experience a drop in velocity, re-examine. After every season, and before a new season begins, re-examine—but leave yourself at least six weeks to correct your weak areas, if possible.

WORK WITH ME

I have helped a great many of baseball players over the last 10+ years with the same information that is written in this book. I've helped them reach their dreams of throwing harder with increased control, getting recruited, drafted, and in my opinion, even saved a few career ending injuries . . . from just a simple exam and simple exercises.

I'm truly excited that this knowledge is finally in your hands, because I imagine once this book is published and available to millions, it's going to be much harder to accommodate everyone who wants more personalized help.

As a special gift to each reader of this book, I invite you to apply to become part of my Elite Baseball Training Group, where I will personally examine you and oversee your training program in my facility to correct your foundational weaknesses. If you choose to stay in the area and work with us on a longer term, I will set you up with one of my trusted strength and conditioning coaches, who will ensure all of your weak areas are strengthened and your goals are met. If you would like a referral to a pitching coach while you are here, I work with many who I trust and are willing to help you.

If you'd be so interested in being part of my Elite Baseball Training Group, I want you to apply with me personally at www.EliteBaseballTrainingGroup.com.

After you apply, someone on my team will give you a call and explain the Elite Program to see if it's a good fit. If it is, we could be working together very soon.

I do hope you enjoyed this book, learned a lot, and it gave you something to think about. It certainly gave you actionable things to do! The world of medicine, rehabilitation, and training is always changing. Be sure to stay up to date and follow me on Twitter @DrChrisMcKenzie. If you see me at a conference, stop me and say hi. I'm very approachable, and I'd love to know how this book impacted you.

I wish you all the best! Many cheers to your future success!

REFERENCES

1. https://redlegnation.com/2015/02/19/running-down-the-velocity-upswing/ Accessed on 5/18/18
2. Kibler, W. B., and J. Chandler. "Baseball and tennis." Rehabilitation of the Injured Knee. St. Louis, MO: Mosby (1995): 219–226.
3. YAMANOUCHI, TOYOAKI. "EMG analysis of the lower extremities during pitching in high-school baseball." The Kurume medical journal 45, no. 1 (1998): 21–25.
4. Campbell, Brian M., David F. Stodden, and Megan K. Nixon. "Lower extremity muscle activation during baseball pitching." The Journal of Strength & Conditioning Research 24, no. 4 (2010): 964–971.
5. McNally, Michael P., John D. Borstad, James A. Oñate, and Ajit MW Chaudhari. "Stride leg ground reaction forces predict throwing velocity in adult recreational baseball pitchers." The Journal of Strength & Conditioning Research 29, no. 10 (2015): 2708–2715.
6. MacWilliams, Bruce A., Tony Choi, Mark K. Perezous, Edmund YS Chao, and Edward G. McFarland. "Characteristic ground-reaction forces in baseball pitching." The American journal of sports medicine 26, no. 1 (1998): 66–71.
7. Escamilla, Rafael F., and James R. Andrews. "Shoulder muscle recruitment patterns and related biomechanics during upper extremity sports." Sports medicine 39, no. 7 (2009): 569–590.
8. DiGiovine, Nick M., Frank W. Jobe, Marilyn Pink, and Jacquelin Perry. "An electromyographic analysis of the upper extremity in pitching." Journal of shoulder and elbow surgery 1, no. 1 (1992): 15–25.
9. Jobe, Frank W., James E. Tibone, Jacquelin Perry, and Diane Moynes. "An EMG analysis of the shoulder in throwing and pitching: a preliminary report." The American journal of sports medicine 11, no. 1 (1983): 3–5.
10. Jobe, Frank W., Diane Radovich Moynes, James E. Tibone, and Jacquelin Perry. "An EMG analysis of the shoulder in pitching: a second report." The American Journal of Sports Medicine 12, no. 3 (1984): 218–220.
11. Werner, Sherry L., Glenn S. Fleisig, Charles J. Dillman, and James R. Andrews. "Biomechanics of the elbow during baseball pitching." Journal of Orthopaedic & Sports Physical Therapy 17, no. 6 (1993): 274–278.
12. Escamilla, Rafael F., Steven W. Barrentine, Glenn S. Fleisig, Naiquan Zheng, Yoshihiro Takada, David Kingsley, and James R. Andrews. "Pitching biomechanics as a pitcher approaches muscular fatigue during a simulated baseball game." The American journal of sports medicine 35, no. 1 (2007): 23–33.
13. Roberts, E. M. "Cinematography in biomechanical investigation." In Proceedings of the CIC Symposium on Biomechanics, 1971, pp. 41–50. The Athletic Institute, 1971.

14. Toyoshima S, Hoshikawa T, Miyashita M, et al. Contribution of the body parts to throwing performance. In: Biomechanics IV. Nelson RC, Morehouse CA, editors. Baltimore, MD: University Part Press, 1974. pp. 169–174

15. Reinold, Michael M., Kevin E. Wilk, Leonard C. Macrina, Chris Sheheane, Shouchen Dun, Glenn S. Fleisig, Ken Crenshaw, and James R. Andrews. "Changes in shoulder and elbow passive range of motion after pitching in professional baseball players." The American journal of sports medicine 36, no. 3 (2008): 523–527.

16. Reuther, Katherine E., Ryan Larsen, Pamela D. Kuhn, John D. Kelly, and Stephen J. Thomas. "Sleeper stretch accelerates recovery of glenohumeral internal rotation after pitching." Journal of shoulder and elbow surgery 25, no. 12 (2016): 1925–1929.

17. Kibler, W. Ben, Aaron Sciascia, and Stephanie Moore. "An acute throwing episode decreases shoulder internal rotation." Clinical Orthopaedics and Related Research® 470, no. 6 (2012): 1545–1551.

18. Burkhart, Stephen S., Craig D. Morgan, and W. Ben Kibler. "The disabled throwing shoulder: spectrum of pathology Part I: pathoanatomy and biomechanics." Arthroscopy 19, no. 4 (2003): 404–420.

19. Shanley, Ellen, Mitchell J. Rauh, Lori A. Michener, Todd S. Ellenbecker, J. Craig Garrison, and Charles A. Thigpen. "Shoulder range of motion measures as risk factors for shoulder and elbow injuries in high school softball and baseball players." The American journal of sports medicine 39, no. 9 (2011): 1997–2006.

20. Tokish, John M., Michael S. Curtin, Young-Kyu Kim, Richard J. Hawkins, and Michael R. Torry. "Glenohumeral internal rotation deficit in the asymptomatic professional pitcher and its relationship to humeral retroversion." Journal of sports science & medicine 7, no. 1 (2008): 78.

21. Wilk, Kevin E., Leonard C. Macrina, Glenn S. Fleisig, Ronald Porterfield, Charles D. Simpson, Paul Harker, Nick Paparesta, and James R. Andrews. "Correlation of glenohumeral internal rotation deficit and total rotational motion to shoulder injuries in professional baseball pitchers." The American journal of sports medicine 39, no. 2 (2011): 329–335.

22. Camp, Christopher L., John M. Zajac, Dave Pearson, Dean Wang, Alec S. Sinatro, Anil S. Ranawat, Joshua S. Dines, and Struan H. Coleman. "The Impact of Workload on the Evolution of Hip Internal and External Rotation in Professional Baseball Players Over the Course of the Season." Orthopaedic journal of sports medicine 6, no. 2 (2018): 2325967117752105.

23. Scher, Steve, Kyle Anderson, Nick Weber, Jeff Bajorek, Kevin Rand, and Michael J. Bey. "Associations among hip and shoulder range of motion and shoulder injury in professional baseball players." Journal of athletic training 45, no. 2 (2010): 191–197.

24. McCulloch, Patrick C., Jayesh K. Patel, Prem N. Ramkumar, Philip C. Noble, and David M. Lintner. "Asymmetric hip rotation in professional baseball pitchers." Orthopaedic Journal of Sports Medicine 2, no. 2 (2014): 2325967114521575.

25. Saito, Manabu, Tomonori Kenmoku, Kentaro Kameyama, Ryo Murata, Takashi Yusa, Nobuyasu Ochiai, Takehiro Kijima et al. "Relationship between tightness of the hip joint and elbow pain in adolescent baseball players." Orthopaedic Journal of Sports Medicine 2, no. 5 (2014): 2325967114532424.

26. Li X, Ma R, Zhou H, Evaluation of hip internal and external rotation range of motion as an injury risk factor for hip, abdominal and groin injuries in professional baseball players. Orthop Rev (Pavia). 7(4). 2015.

27. Fleisig, Glenn S., James R. Andrews, Charles J. Dillman, and Rafael F. Escamilla. "Kinetics of baseball pitching with implications about injury mechanisms." The American journal of sports medicine 23, no. 2 (1995): 233–239.

28. Chalmers, Peter N., Markus A. Wimmer, Nikhil N. Verma, Brian J. Cole, Anthony A. Romeo, Gregory L. Cvetanovich, Michael L. Pearl et al. "The Relationship Between Pitching Mechanics and Injury: A Review of Current Concepts." Sports health 9, no. 3 (2017): 216–221.

29. Wilk, Kevin E., Leonard C. Macrina, Glenn S. Fleisig, Kyle T. Aune, Ron A. Porterfield, Paul Harker, Timothy J. Evans, and James R. Andrews. "Deficits in glenohumeral passive range of motion increase risk of elbow injury in professional baseball pitchers: a prospective study." The American journal of sports medicine 42, no. 9 (2014): 2075–2081.

30. Wilk, Kevin E., Leonard C. Macrina, Glenn S. Fleisig, Kyle T. Aune, Ron A. Porterfield, Paul Harker, Timothy J. Evans, and James R. Andrews. "Deficits in glenohumeral passive range of motion increase risk of shoulder injury in professional baseball pitchers: a prospective study." The American journal of sports medicine 43, no. 10 (2015): 2379–2385.

31. Clabbers, Kim M., John D. Kelly, Dov Bader, Matthew Eager, Carl Imhauser, Sorin Siegler, and Ray A. Moyer. "Effect of posterior capsule tightness on glenohumeral translation in the late-cocking phase of pitching." Journal of sport rehabilitation 16, no. 1 (2007): 41–49.

32. Shanley, Ellen, Mitchell J. Rauh, Lori A. Michener, Todd S. Ellenbecker, J. Craig Garrison, and Charles A. Thigpen. "Shoulder range of motion measures as risk factors for shoulder and elbow injuries in high school softball and baseball players." The American journal of sports medicine 39, no. 9 (2011): 1997–2006.

33. Conway, John. "Labrum and Biceps Tendon Pathology in Throwers." Slide deck, ASMI 35th Annual Injuries in Baseball Course, Dallas, TX, January 26–29, 2017.

34. Miniaci, Anthony, Anthony T. Mascia, David C. Salonen, and Edna J. Becker. "Magnetic resonance imaging of the shoulder in asymptomatic professional baseball pitchers." The American journal of sports medicine 30, no. 1 (2002): 66–73.

35. Dillman, Charles J., Glenn S. Fleisig, and James R. Andrews. "Biomechanics of pitching with emphasis upon shoulder kinematics." Journal of Orthopaedic & Sports Physical Therapy 18, no. 2 (1993): 402–408.

36. Seroyer, Shane T., Shane J. Nho, Bernard R. Bach, Charles A. Bush-Joseph, Gregory P. Nicholson, and Anthony A. Romeo. "The kinetic chain in overhand pitching: its potential role for performance enhancement and injury prevention." Sports health 2, no. 2 (2010): 135–146.

37. Fleisig, Glenn S., James R. Andrews, Charles J. Dillman, and Rafael F. Escamilla. "Kinetics of baseball pitching with implications about injury mechanisms." The American journal of sports medicine 23, no. 2 (1995): 233–239.

38. Morrey, Bernard F., and Kai-Nan An. "Articular and ligamentous contributions to the stability of the elbow joint." The American journal of sports medicine 11, no. 5 (1983): 315–319.

39. Dillman, C. J. "Valgus extension overload in baseball pitching." Med. Sci. Sports Exerc. 23 (1991): S153.

40. Begly, John P., Michael S. Guss, Theodore S. Wolfson, Siddharth A. Mahure, Andrew S. Rokito, and Laith M. Jazrawi. "Performance outcomes after medial ulnar collateral ligament reconstruction in Major League Baseball positional players." Journal of shoulder and elbow surgery 27, no. 2 (2018): 282–290.

41. Erickson, Brandon J., Anil K. Gupta, Joshua D. Harris, Charles Bush-Joseph, Bernard R. Bach, Geoffrey D. Abrams, Angielyn M. San Juan, Brian J. Cole, and Anthony A. Romeo. "Rate of return to pitching and performance after Tommy John surgery in Major League Baseball pitchers." The American journal of sports medicine 42, no. 3 (2014): 536–543.

42. Peters, Scott D., Garrett S. Bullock, Adam P. Goode, Grant E. Garrigues, David S. Ruch, and Michael P. Reiman. "The success of return to sport after ulnar collateral ligament injury in baseball: a systematic review and meta-analysis." Journal of shoulder and elbow surgery 27, no. 3 (2018): 561–571.

43. Rebolledo, Brian J., Jeffrey R. Dugas, Asheesh Bedi, Michael G. Ciccotti, David W. Altchek, and Joshua S. Dines. "Avoiding Tommy John Surgery: What Are the Alternatives?." The American journal of sports medicine 45, no. 13 (2017): 3143–3148.

44. Magnusson, S. PETER, GILBERT W. Gleim, and JAMES A. Nicholas. "Shoulder weakness in professional baseball pitchers." Medicine and science in sports and exercise 26, no. 1 (1994): 5–9.

45. Mehdi, Syed K., Salvatore J. Frangiamore, and Mark S. Schickendantz. "Latissimus dorsi and teres major injuries in major league baseball pitchers: a systematic review." Am J Orthop 45, no. 3 (2016): 163–167.

46. Myers, Joseph B. "USA Baseball Long Term Development." Slide deck, Penn Throwing Symposium, Philadelphia, PA. January, 2018.

47. Pexa, Brett S., Eric D. Ryan, Elizabeth E. Hibberd, Elizabeth Teel, Terri Jo Rucinski, and Joseph B. Myers. "Infraspinatus Cross Sectional Area and Shoulder Range of Motion Change Following Live-Game Baseball Pitching." Journal of sport rehabilitation (2017): 1–26.

48. Trakis, James E., Malachy P. McHugh, Philip A. Caracciolo, Lisa Busciacco, Michael Mullaney, and Stephen J. Nicholas. "Muscle strength and range of motion in adolescent pitchers with throwing-related pain: implications for injury prevention." The American journal of sports medicine 36, no. 11 (2008): 2173–2178.

49. Tyler, Timothy F., Michael J. Mullaney, Michael R. Mirabella, Stephen J. Nicholas, and Malachy P. McHugh. "Risk factors for shoulder and elbow injuries in high school baseball pitchers: the role of preseason strength and range of motion." The American journal of sports medicine 42, no. 8 (2014): 1993–1999.

50. Byram, Ian R., Brandon D. Bushnell, Keith Dugger, Kevin Charron, Frank E. Harrell Jr, and Thomas J. Noonan. "Preseason shoulder strength measurements in professional baseball pitchers: identifying players at risk for injury." The American journal of sports medicine 38, no. 7 (2010): 1375–1382.

51. Yang J, Mann BJ, Guettler JH, et al. Risk-Prone Pitching Activities and Injuries in Youth Baseball: Findings From a National Sample. Am J Sports Med. 2014;42(6):1456–1463.

52. Lyman, Stephen, Glenn S. Fleisig, James R. Andrews, and E. David Osinski. "Effect of pitch type, pitch count, and pitching mechanics on risk of elbow and shoulder pain in youth baseball pitchers." The American journal of sports medicine 30, no. 4 (2002): 463–468.

53. Olsen, Samuel J., Glenn S. Fleisig, Shouchen Dun, Jeremy Loftice, and James R. Andrews. "Risk factors for shoulder and elbow injuries in adolescent baseball pitchers." The American journal of sports medicine 34, no. 6 (2006): 905–912.

54. Yang, Jingzhen, Barton J. Mann, Joseph H. Guettler, Jeffrey R. Dugas, James J. Irrgang, Glenn S. Fleisig, and John P. Albright. "Risk-prone pitching activities and injuries in youth baseball: findings from a national sample." The American journal of sports medicine 42, no. 6 (2014): 1456–1463.

55. Fleisig, Glenn S., James R. Andrews, Gary R. Cutter, Adam Weber, Jeremy Loftice, Chris McMichael, Nina Hassell, and Stephen Lyman. "Risk of serious injury for young baseball pitchers: a 10-year prospective study." The American journal of sports medicine 39, no. 2 (2011): 253–257.

56. Fleisig, Glenn S., and James R. Andrews. "Prevention of elbow injuries in youth baseball pitchers." Sports health 4, no. 5 (2012): 419–424.

57. Bandy, William D., and Jean M. Irion. "The effect of time on static stretch on the flexibility of the hamstring muscles." Physical therapy 74, no. 9 (1994): 845–850.

58. Bandy, William D., Jean M. Irion, and Michelle Briggler. "The effect of time and frequency of static stretching on flexibility of the hamstring muscles." Physical therapy 77, no. 10 (1997): 1090–1096.

59. McMillian, Danny J., Josef H. Moore, Brian S. Hatler, and Dean C. Taylor. "Dynamic vs. static-stretching warm up: the effect on power and agility performance." The Journal of Strength & Conditioning Research 20, no. 3 (2006): 492–499.

60. Taylor, Kristie-Lee, Jeremy M. Sheppard, Hamilton Lee, and Norma Plummer. "Negative effect of static stretching restored when combined with a sport specific warm-up component." Journal of Science and Medicine in Sport 12, no. 6 (2009): 657–661.

61. Yamaguchi, Taichi, and Kojiro Ishii. "Effects of static stretching for 30 seconds and dynamic stretching on leg extension power." Journal of Strength and Conditioning Research 19, no. 3 (2005): 677.

62. Perrier, Erica T., Michael J. Pavol, and Mark A. Hoffman. "The acute effects of a warm-up including static or dynamic stretching on countermovement jump height, reaction time, and flexibility." The Journal of Strength & Conditioning Research 25, no. 7 (2011): 1925–1931.

63. Trumbo, Paula, Sandra Schlicker, Allison A. Yates, and Mary Poos. "Dietary reference intakes for energy, carbohydrate, fiber, fat, fatty acids, cholesterol, protein and amino acids." Journal of the American Dietetic Association 102, no. 11 (2002): 1621–1630.

64. https://www.mayoclinic.org/healthy-lifestyle/nutrition-and-healthy-eating/in-depth/water/art-20044256 Accessed on 4/3/18.

65. Warren, Courtney D., David J. Szymanski, and Merrill R. Landers. "Effects of three recovery protocols on range of motion, heart rate, rating of perceived exertion, and blood lactate in baseball pitchers during a simulated game." The Journal of Strength & Conditioning Research 29, no. 11 (2015): 3016–3025.

66. University of California - Berkeley. "Lactic Acid Not Athlete's Poison, But An Energy Source -- If You Know How To Use It." ScienceDaily. www.sciencedaily. com/releases/2006/04/060420235214.htm (accessed May 23, 2018).

67. Kibler, W. Ben, Tim L. Uhl, Jackson WQ Maddux, Paul V. Brooks, Brian Zeller, and John McMullen. "Qualitative clinical evaluation of scapular dysfunction: a reliability study." Journal of Shoulder and Elbow Surgery 11, no. 6 (2002): 550–556.

68. Edelson, Gordon. "Variations in the retroversion of the humeral head." Journal of shoulder and elbow surgery 8, no. 2 (1999): 142–145.

69. Noonan, Thomas J., Charles A. Thigpen, Lane B. Bailey, Douglas J. Wyland, Michael Kissenberth, Richard J. Hawkins, and Ellen Shanley. "Humeral torsion as a risk factor for shoulder and elbow injury in professional baseball pitchers." The American journal of sports medicine 44, no. 9 (2016): 2214–2219.

70. Fleisig, Glenn S., Becky Bolt, Dave Fortenbaugh, Kevin E. Wilk, and James R. Andrews. "Biomechanical comparison of baseball pitching and long-toss: implications for training and rehabilitation." journal of orthopaedic & sports physical therapy 41, no. 5 (2011): 296–303.

71. Slenker, Nicholas R., Orr Limpisvasti, Karen Mohr, Arnel Aguinaldo, and Neal S. ElAttrache. "Biomechanical comparison of the interval throwing program and baseball pitching: upper extremity loads in training and rehabilitation." The American journal of sports medicine 42, no. 5 (2014): 1226–1232.

72. https://www.littleleague.org/partnerships/pitch-smart/overuse-primary-cause-arm-injuries/ Accessed 5/26/18 According to grant research: Injuries to Youth Pitchers in Baseball. Mueller FO (PI), Marshall SW, Goldberg B. Agency: Yawkey Foundation. 3/1/06 - 2/28/11.

73. Erickson, Brandon J., Peter N. Chalmers, Michael J. Axe, and Anthony A. Romeo. "Exceeding pitch count recommendations in little league baseball increases the chance of requiring Tommy John surgery as a professional baseball pitcher." Orthopaedic Journal of Sports Medicine 5, no. 3 (2017): 2325967117695085.

74. http://m.mlb.com/pitchsmart/pitching-guidelines/ Accessed on 4/17/18

75. Fleisig, Glenn S., Alek Z. Diffendaffer, Kyle T. Aune, Brett Ivey, and Walter A. Laughlin. "Biomechanical analysis of weighted-ball exercises for baseball pitchers." Sports health 9, no. 3 (2017): 210–215.

76. Reinold, Mike, Leonard Macrina, Kyle Aune, Glenn S. Fleisig, and James Andrews. "The Effect Of A 6-week Weighted-ball Throwing Program On Pitching Velocity And Arm Stress." journal of Orthopaedic & Sports Physical 47, no. 1 (2017): A206.

77. Myers, Joseph B., Sakiko Oyama, and Elizabeth E. Hibberd. "Scapular dysfunction in high school baseball players sustaining throwing-related upper extremity injury: a prospective study." Journal of shoulder and elbow surgery 22, no. 9 (2013): 1154–1159.

78. Laudner, Kevin G., Mike T. Moline, and Keith Meister. "The relationship between forward scapular posture and posterior shoulder tightness among baseball players." The American journal of sports medicine 38, no. 10 (2010): 2106–2112.

ABOUT THE AUTHOR

As a former athlete, Dr. Chris McKenzie (board certified specialist in sports and orthopedic physical therapy) knows the detriments of poor, unskilled training. In more than 10 years of practice, he has helped hundreds of baseball pitchers achieve their full potential: throwing over 90 mph with a repeatable, healthy delivery. They are now playing in elite college programs, in almost every major league organization, and in top youth programs nationwide. He has been an adjunct professor at Drexel University and owns McKenzie Sports Physical Therapy in Philadelphia, PA.

Chris received his bachelor's of science in Kinesiology from Penn State University and his clinical doctorate in Physical Therapy from Drexel University. He lives with his wife, Emma, and son, Graham, in Philadelphia. They all enjoy regular exercise and being outdoors. Chris claims he can now "die happy" as the Philadelphia Eagles have finally won a Super Bowl.

You've got your exam results. You know what areas need to be addressed to unleash your pitching velocity. You only have one thing left to do. . . . Get your unique corrective strength program and watch the MPH add up, and the hitters go down. Head to www.CommandThePlate.com

- Build your COMPLETE program unique to your BASE-3 exam results
- Over 100 video exercise progressions
- Build strength exactly where you need it
- Get more flexibility exactly where you need it
- Increase your dynamic control and command the plate!
- Learn the proper way to exercise, and what form to avoid.
- Access online, anywhere you have internet.
- Watch again and again until you are comfortable with the exercise, or get a quick reminder.
- Get started now, at www.CommandThePlate.com

Not a fan of following words and lists? Are pictures worth a thousand words and even more ways to screw it up? We've got what you need! See exactly how Dr. McKenzie examine's his ball players by watching him do the BASE-3 Examination on video!

- Learn and mimic his exact pressure and hand positions for the best results
- Get his insider tips on how he interprets certain hard to read test results.
- Watch Dr McKenzie do it, hear him explain it, then accurately do the test yourself.
- Watch it again and again, whenever you need it, whereever you have internet access.
- Use is every season.
- Head to www.Base3Examination.com

24731191R00118

Made in the USA
Lexington, KY
18 December 2018